PRINTED TEST BANK

William Timberlake
Los Angeles Harbor College

G. Lynn Carlson
University of Wisconsin, Parkside

CHEMISTRY
An Introduction to General, Organic, and Biological Chemistry

Karen C. Timberlake

D1274878

TENTH EDITION

PEARSON

Prentice
Hall

Upper Saddle River, NJ 07458

Editor-in-Chief, Science: Nicole Folchetti
Senior Editor: Kent Porter Hamann
Assistant Editor: Jessica Neumann
Assistant Managing Editor, Science: Gina M. Cheselka
Project Manager, Science: Ashley M. Booth
Supplement Cover Manager: Paul Gourhan
Supplement Cover Designer: Victoria Colotta
Operations Specialist: Amanda Smith
Director of Operations: Barbara Kittle

© 2009 Pearson Education, Inc.
Pearson Prentice Hall
Pearson Education, Inc.
Upper Saddle River, NJ 07458

Printed in the United States of America

10 9 8 7 6 5 4 3 2 1

ISBN-13: 978-0-13-500907-9

ISBN-10:   0-13-500907-3

Pearson Education Ltd., *London*
Pearson Education Australia Pty. Ltd., *Sydney*
Pearson Education Singapore, Pte. Ltd.
Pearson Education North Asia Ltd., *Hong Kong*
Pearson Education Canada, Inc., *Toronto*
Pearson Educación de Mexico, S.A. de C.V.
Pearson Education—Japan, *Tokyo*
Pearson Education Malaysia, Pte. Ltd.

Contents

Prologue

P.1 Multiple Choice Questions

1) Water, H_2O, is an example of a(n) _____.
   A) chemical
   B) solid
   C) wave
   D) electric charge
   E) element

   Answer: A

2) In this list, which substance can be classified as a chemical?
   A) salt
   B) sleep
   C) cold
   D) heat
   E) temperature

   Answer: A

3) One example of a chemical used in toothpaste is _____.
   A) chlorine
   B) sulfur
   C) carbon dioxide
   D) calcium carbonate
   E) sugar

   Answer: D

4) Which of the following is not a chemical?
   A) salt
   B) water
   C) light
   D) carbon dioxide
   E) sugar

   Answer: C

5) Sodium monofluorophosphate is a chemical used in toothpaste to _____.
   A) make the paste white
   B) disinfect the toothbrush
   C) keep the paste from spoiling
   D) remove plaque
   E) strengthen tooth enamel

   Answer: E

6) Chlorofluorocarbons are broken down in the atmosphere by _____.
   A) nitrogen dioxide
   B) ozone
   C) iron
   D) AIDS
   E) ultraviolet light

Answer: E

7) When a part of the body is injured, substances called _____. are released.
   A) aspirins
   B) pain relievers
   C) nitrogen oxides
   D) chlorofluorocarbons
   E) prostaglandins

Answer: E

8) The production of smog from the chemical NO requires _____.
   A) nitrogen   B) chlorine   C) water   D) oxygen   E) CFCs

Answer: D

9) When scientific information is used for industrial purposes, the discipline is known as _____.
   A) the scientific method
   B) marketing
   C) commercial
   D) hypothetical
   E) technology

Answer: E

10) Employing scientific information to develop new materials to benefit society is an example of _____.
   A) technology
   B) philosophy
   C) marketing
   D) sociology
   E) politics

Answer: A

11) DDT is a type of _____.
   A) herbicide
   B) war gas
   C) plant
   D) insecticide
   E) metal

Answer: D

12) Chlorofluorocarbons are destructive to the _____.
   A) ozone produced at ground level in traffic
   B) water in the upper atmosphere
   C) nitrogen dioxide in smog
   D) ozone layer in the upper atmosphere
   E) copper in telephone wiring

   Answer: D

13) Titanium dioxide is a chemical used in toothpaste to _____.
   A) make the paste white
   B) disinfect the toothbrush
   C) keep the paste from spoiling
   D) remove plaque
   E) strengthen tooth enamel

   Answer: A

14) The first step in the scientific imethod is _____.
   A) using technology
   B) making observations
   C) forming a hypothesis
   D) doing experiments
   E) proposing a theory

   Answer: B

15) DDT was a good pesticide because _____.
   A) it had low toxicity to animals
   B) it was cheap to prepare
   C) it was toxic to many insects
   D) it had low toxicity to humans
   E) all the above

   Answer: E

16) One way to enhance your learning in chemistry is to _____.
   A) study a little every day
   B) form a study group
   C) go to office hours
   D) be an active learner
   E) all the above

   Answer: E

17) You notice that there is more traffic between 8 and 9 in the morning. This would be a(n)
   _____.
   A) observation
   B) hypothesis
   C) experiment
   D) theory
   E) all the above

   Answer: A

18) There is more traffic between 8 and 9 in the morning because most people start work at 9. This would be a(n) _____.
   A) observation
   B) hypothesis
   C) experiment
   D) theory
   E) all the above

Answer: B

19) In order to enhance your learning in chemistry, you should not _____.
   A) study a little every day
   B) form a study group
   C) go to office hours
   D) be an active learner
   E) wait until the night before the exam to study

Answer: E

20) Which of the following is a chemical?
   A) sugar   B) heat   C) light   D) noise   E) a wave

Answer: A

P.2 True/False Questions

1) The reddish–brown color of smog is due to NO_2.

Answer: TRUE

2) Chloroflourocarbons are broken down in the upper atmosphere to produce oxygen, O_2.

Answer: FALSE

3) DDT is effective against poison ivy.

Answer: FALSE

4) The first step in using the scientific method is usually the observation of some natural event.

Answer: TRUE

5) In the scientific method, a hypothesis has more data to support it than a theory.

Answer: FALSE

6) Titanium dioxide in toothpaste is used as a detergent.

Answer: FALSE

7) A theory is confirmed after one experiment is performed.

Answer: FALSE

8) Alchemists believed there were four components of nature: earth, fire, air, and water.

Answer: TRUE

9) Working with a group of studenst can help you learn chemistry.

Answer: TRUE

10) Paracelsus was a Greek philosopher.
    Answer: FALSE

11) DDT was banned because it breaks down quickly in the environment.
    Answer: FALSE

P.3 Short Answer Questions

1) A chemical that consists of one type of matter and always has the same composition and properties is called a _____.
   Answer: substance

2) The brown color of smog is caused by _____.
   Answer: nitrogen dioxide

3) The use of observation and hypothesis are important steps in the _____ method.
   Answer: scientific

4) DDT is an effective pesticide against _____.
   Answer: insects

5) A test performed to determine if a hypothesis is valid is called a(n) _____.
   Answer: experiment

6) A hypothesis can be tested by performing a(n) _____.
   Answer: experiment

7) Any material used in or produced by a chemical reaction is a _____.
   Answer: chemical

8) An observation takes place when a(n) _____ is noted.
   Answer: natural phenomenon

9) Name the steps in the scientific method.
   Answer: observation, hypothesis, experiment, theory

10) When scientific principles are used to produce consumer goods, the discipline is termed _____.
    Answer: technology

11) An abrasive used in toothpaste is _____.
    Answer: calcium carbonate

12) When a hypothesis is supported by many experiments is becomes a _____.
    Answer: theory

13) The science that studies the properties and composition of substances is called _____.
    Answer: chemistry

14) In the scientific method, after data is collected, a _____ is proposed which gives a possible explanation.
    Answer: hypothesis

15) The substance the alchemists thought could turn metals into gold was called _____ .
    Answer: the philosopher's stone

16) The substances released when tissues are injured are _____.
    Answer: prostaglandins

17) Substances which prevent spoilage are called _____.
    Answer: antioxidants

18) The chemical used to make cans and foil is _____.
    Answer: aluminum

Chapter 1 Measurements

1.1 Multiple-Choice Questions

1) 5.21 cm is the same distance as
   A) 0.0521 m.
   B) 52.1 dm.
   C) 5.21 mm.
   D) 0.00521 km.
   E) 5210 m.

Answer: A

2) How many centimeters are there in 57.0 in.?
   A) 22 cm   B) 0.0445 cm   C) 145 cm   D) 22.4 cm   E) 140 cm

Answer: C

3) The amount of space occupied by a substance is its
   A) mass.   B) density.   C) weight.   D) length.   E) volume.

Answer: E

4) Which of the following is the basic unit of volume in the metric system?
   A) liter
   B) kilogram
   C) meter
   D) centimeter
   E) gram

Answer: A

5) Which of the following is a measurement of mass in the metric system?
   A) milliliter
   B) centimeter
   C) kilogram
   D) Celsius
   E) meter

Answer: C

6) A value of 25 °C is a measurement of
   A) distance.
   B) volume.
   C) temperature.
   D) mass.
   E) density.

Answer: C

7) A value of 36 mL is a measure of
    A) density
    B) mass
    C) temperature
    D) volume
    E) distance

Answer: D

8) A value of 345 mm is a measure of
    A) density
    B) mass
    C) temperature
    D) volume
    E) distance

Answer: E

9) The measurement 0.000 004 3 m, expressed correctly using scientific notation, is
    A) 4.3×10^{-7} m.
    B) 4.3×10^{-6} m.
    C) 4.3×10^{6} m.
    D) 0.43×10^{-5} m.
    E) 4.3 m.

Answer: B

10) Which of the following conversion factors is a measured number?
    A) 10 cm/dm
    B) 12 in/ft
    C) 16 oz/lb
    D) 25 miles/gallon
    E) 12 eggs/dozen

Answer: D

11) The measurement of the gravitational pull on an object is its
    A) volume.   B) weight.   C) mass.   D) length.   E) size.

Answer: B

12) Which of the following measurements has three significant figures?
    A) 0.005 m   B) 510 m   C) 0.510 m   D) 0.051 m   E) 5100 m

Answer: C

13) 1.00 pint of milk has a volume of how many milliliters? (2 pints = 1 quart)
    A) 472 mL   B) 530. mL   C) 1000 mL   D) 1890 mL   E) 106 mL

Answer: A

14) Which of the following numbers contains the designated CORRECT number of significant figures?

A) 0.04300   5 significant figures
B) 0.00302   2 significant figures
C) 156 000   3 significant figures
D) 1.04   2 significant figures
E) 3.0650   4 significant figures

Answer: C

15) The number of significant figures in the measurement of 45.030 mm is

A) none.   B) three.   C) four.   D) five.   E) six.

Answer: D

16) How many significant figures are in the number 0.00208?

A) six   B) two   C) three   D) four   E) five

Answer: C

17) Which of the following examples illustrates a number that is correctly rounded to three significant figures?

A) 4.05438 grams to 4.054 grams
B) 0.03954 grams to 0.040 grams
C) 103.692 grams to 103.7 grams
D) 109 526 grams to 109 500 grams
E) 20.0332 grams to 20.0 grams

Answer: E

18) A calculator answer of 423.6059 must be rounded off to three significant figures. What answer is reported?

A) 423   B) 424   C) 420   D) 423.6   E) 423.7

Answer: B

19) Which of the answers for the following conversions contains the correct number of significant figures?

A) $2.543 \text{ m} \times \dfrac{39.4 \text{ in}}{1 \text{ m}} = 100.1942 \text{ in}$

B) $2 \text{ L} \times \dfrac{1.06 \text{ qt}}{1 \text{ L}} = 2.12 \text{ qt}$

C) $24.95 \text{ min} \times \dfrac{1 \text{ hr}}{60 \text{ min}} = 0.4158 \text{ hr}$

D) $12.0 \text{ ft} \times \dfrac{12 \text{ in.}}{1 \text{ ft}} \times \dfrac{2.54 \text{ cm}}{1 \text{ in}} = 370 \text{ cm}$

E) $24.0 \text{ kg} \times \dfrac{1 \text{ lb}}{2.20 \text{ kg}} = 11 \text{ lb}$

Answer: C

20) What is the correct answer for the calculation of a volume (in mL) with measured numbers $\dfrac{28.58}{16 \times 8.02}$?

A) 0.22 mL   B) 0.223 mL   C) 57 mL   D) 14 mL   E) 14.3 mL

Answer: A

21) When 2610 + 11.7 + 0.22 are added, the answer to the correct number of decimal places is
   A) 2621.92
   B) 2621.9
   C) 2621
   D) 2620
   E) 2600

   Answer: D

22) What is the answer, with the correct number of decimal places, for this problem?

   4.392 g + 102.40 g + 2.51 g =
   A) 109.302 g   B) 109 g   C) 109.3 g   D) 109.30 g   E) 110 g

   Answer: D

23) The correct answer for the addition of 7.5 g + 2.26 g + 1.311 g + 2 g is
   A) 13.071 g.   B) 13 g.   C) 13.0 g.   D) 10 g.   E) 13.1 g.

   Answer: B

24) Which of the following measurements are NOT equivalent?
   A) 25 mg = 0.025 g
   B) 183 L = 0.183 kL
   C) 150 msec = 0.150 sec
   D) 84 cm = 8.4 mm
   E) 24 dL = 2.4 L

   Answer: D

25) In which of the following is the metric unit paired with its correct abbreviation?
   A) microgram / mg
   B) milliliter / mL
   C) centimeter / km
   D) kilogram / cg
   E) gram / gm

   Answer: B

26) Which of the following is the largest unit?
   A) millimeter
   B) micrometer
   C) meter
   D) decimeter
   E) kilometer

   Answer: E

27) What is the metric relationship between grams and micrograms?
   A) 1 g = 100 μg
   B) 1 g = 1 000 000 μg
   C) 1 g = 0.000 001 μg
   D) 1 g = 1000 μg
   E) 1 g = 0.001 μg

   Answer: B

28) What is the conversion factor for the relationship between millimeters and centimeters?
    A) 1 mm/1 cm
    B) 10 mm/1 cm
    C) 1 cm/1 mm
    D) 100 mm/1 cm
    E) 10 cm/1 mm
    Answer: B

29) Which of the following is the smallest unit?
    A) gram
    B) milligram
    C) kilogram
    D) decigram
    E) microgram
    Answer: E

30) The cubic centimeter (cm^3 or cc) has the same volume as a
    A) cubic inch.
    B) cubic liter.
    C) milliliter.
    D) centimeter.
    E) cubic decimeter.
    Answer: C

31) 9.31 g is the same mass as
    A) 931 µg.
    B) 931 kg.
    C) 93.1 cg.
    D) 9310 mg.
    E) 0.0931 dg.
    Answer: D

32) According to the United States Food and Drug Administration, the recommended daily requirement of protein is 44 g. This is _____ of protein.
    A) 1248.5 oz
    B) 320 000 oz
    C) 1.6 oz
    D) 0.0605 oz
    E) 150 000 oz
    Answer: C

33) Which of the following setups would convert centimeters to feet?

A) $cm \times \dfrac{2.54 \text{ in.}}{1 \text{ cm}} \times \dfrac{1 \text{ ft}}{12 \text{ in.}}$

B) $cm \times \dfrac{2.54 \text{ cm}}{1 \text{ in.}} \times \dfrac{12 \text{ in.}}{1 \text{ ft}}$

C) $cm \times \dfrac{1 \text{ in.}}{2.54 \text{ cm}} \times \dfrac{1 \text{ ft}}{12 \text{ in.}}$

D) $cm \times \dfrac{1 \text{ in.}}{2.54 \text{ cm}} \times \dfrac{12 \text{ in.}}{1 \text{ ft}}$

E) $cm \times \dfrac{2.54 \text{ cm}}{1 \text{ in.}} \times \dfrac{1 \text{ ft}}{12 \text{ in.}}$

Answer: C

34) A conversion factor set up correctly to convert 15 inches to centimeters is
    A) 100 cm/1 m.
    B) 1 inch/2.54 cm.
    C) 1 cm/10 mm.
    D) 2.54 cm/1 inch.
    E) 10 cm/1 inch.
Answer: D

35) How many pounds are in 3.5 kg?
    A) 7.7 lb   B) 1.59 lb   C) 0.629 lb   D) 1.6 lb   E) 7.70 lb
Answer: A

36) How many liters of soft drink are there in 5.25 qt?
    A) 4950 L   B) 55.7 L   C) 4.95 L   D) 5.57 L   E) 5.0 L
Answer: C

37) What is 6.5 m converted to inches?
    A) 1700 in   B) 1651 in   C) 39 in   D) 260 in   E) 255.9 in
Answer: D

38) How many kilograms are in 30.4 lb?
    A) 13.8 kg   B) 14 kg   C) 67 kg   D) 66.88 kg   E) 66.9 kg
Answer: A

39) A nugget of gold with a mass of 521 g is added to 50.0 mL of water. The water level rises to a volume of 77.0 mL. What is the density of the gold?
    A) 10.4 g/mL
    B) 6.77 g/mL
    C) 1.00 g/mL
    D) 0.0518 g/mL
    E) 19.3 g/mL
Answer: E

40) A dose of aspirin of 5.0 mg per kilogram of body weight has been prescribed to reduce the fever of an infant weighing 8.5 pounds. The number of milligrams of aspirin that should be administered is
    A) 19 mg.   B) 53 mg.   C) 1.6 mg.   D) 5.0 mg.   E) 0.59 mg.

Answer: A

41) A doctor's order is 0.125 g of ampicillin. The liquid suspension on hand contains 250 mg/5.0 mL. How many milliliters of the suspension are required?
    A) 0.0025 mL
    B) 3.0 mL
    C) 2.5 mL
    D) 6.3 mL
    E) 0.0063 mL

Answer: C

42) Which one of the following substances will float in gasoline, which has a density of 0.66 g/mL?
    A) table salt   (d = 2.16 g/mL)
    B) balsa wood   (d = 0.16 g/mL)
    C) sugar   (d = 1.59 g/mL)
    D) aluminum   (d = 2.70 g/mL)
    E) mercury   (d = 13.6 g/mL)

Answer: B

43) What is the mass of 2.00 L of an intravenous glucose solution with a density of 1.15 g/mL?
    A) 0.023 kg   B) 2.30 kg   C) 1.15 kg   D) 0.015 kg   E) 0.58 kg

Answer: B

44) Mercury has a specific gravity of 13.6. How many milliliters of mercury have a mass of 0.35 kg?
    A) 0.0257 mL
    B) 0.026 mL
    C) 25.7 mL
    D) 26 mL
    E) 4760 mL

Answer: D

45) What is the density of a substance with a mass of 45.00 g and a volume of 26.4 mL?
    A) 1.70 g/mL
    B) 1.7 g/mL
    C) 0.59 g/mL
    D) 0.587 g/mL
    E) 45.0 g/mL

Answer: A

46) What is the mass of 53 mL of ethyl alcohol, which has a density of 0.79 g/mL?
    A) 67.1 g   B) 41.9 g   C) 42 g   D) 67 g   E) 53 g

Answer: C

47) A liquid has a volume of 34.6 mL and a mass of 46.0 g. What is the density of the liquid?
   A) 1.00 g/mL
   B) 1.33 g/mL
   C) 0.752 g/mL
   D) 1330 g/mL
   E) 0.663 g/mL

Answer: B

48) The density of a solution is 1.18 g/mL. Its specific gravity is
   A) 11.8.   B) 0.118.   C) 0.847.   D) 1.18.   E) 1.2.

Answer: D

49) Diamond has a density of 3.52 g/mL. What is the volume in cubic centimeters of a diamond with a mass of 15.1 g?
   A) 4.3 cm^3
   B) 4.29 cm^3
   C) 0.233 cm^3
   D) 53 cm^3
   E) 53.2 cm^3

Answer: B

50) The ratio of the mass of a substance to its volume is its
   A) specific gravity.
   B) density.
   C) buoyancy.
   D) weight.
   E) conversion factor.

Answer: B

51) The EPA limit for lead in the soil of play areas is 400 ppm. This is the same as
   A) 400 mg lead in each gram of soil.
   B) 400 g lead in each kilogram of soil.
   C) 400 mg lead in each kilogram of soil.
   D) 400 μg lead in each kilogram of soil.
   E) 400 μg lead in each milligram of soil.

Answer: C

52) Which of the following is often used to determine an individual's percentage of body fat?
   A) temperature
   B) height
   C) weight loss
   D) weight gain
   E) density

Answer: E

53) A 50.0 mL urine sample has a mass of 50.7 g. The specific gravity of the urine is
   A) 1.014 g/mL.
   B) 0.986 g/L.
   C) 1.01.
   D) 0.986.
   E) 50.7.
   Answer: C

1.2 Short Answer Questions

Round off each of the following to three significant figures.
   1) 504.85
      Answer: 505

   2) 8.3158
      Answer: 8.32

   3) 25 225
      Answer: 25 200

   4) 6.3477×10^4
      Answer: 6.35×10^4

   5) 399870
      Answer: 4.00×10^5

   6) 58.5422
      Answer: 58.5

   7) 0.003 4088
      Answer: 0.00341

Express each of the following numbers using scientific notation.
   8) 351 000 000 000
      Answer: 3.51×10^{11}

   9) 0.000 860
      Answer: 8.60×10^{-4}

   10) 5 207 000
      Answer: 5.207×10^6

   11) 0.000 000 050
      Answer: 5.0×10^{-8}

State the number of significant figures in each of the following measurements.
   12) 0.705 m
      Answer: 3

13) 680 000 km

Answer: 2

14) 0.008090 cm

Answer: 4

15) 28.050 km

Answer: 5

16) 0.0005 L

Answer: 1

17) 75.00 m

Answer: 4

18) 2.043×10^4 mm

Answer: 4

19) 6.1×10^{-5} mL

Answer: 2

20) 9.00×10^6 g

Answer: 3

1.3 Matching Questions

Are the numbers in each of the following statements measured or exact?

1) In the U.S. system there are 12 inches in one foot.

A) exact

B) measured

2) The patient's blood sugar level is 350 mg/dL.

3) There are 452 pages in a book.

4) The rabbit weighs 2.5 pounds.

5) 1 liter is equal to 1.06 quarts.

6) There are 100 capsules in the bottle.

7) The patient's temperature is 100.1 °F.

8) I lost 14 pounds on my diet last month.

| 1) A | 2) B | 3) A | 4) B | 5) B | 6) A |
| 7) B | 8) B | | | | |

Match the type of measurement to the unit given below.

9) milliliter   A) temperature

10) mm   B) density

11) gram   C) mass

12) 125 K   D) volume

13) kilometer   E) distance

14) milligram

9) D   10) E   11) C   12) A   13) E   14) C

Select the correct prefix to complete the equality.

15) 1 mL = _____ L   A) 100

16) 1 m = _____ mm   B) 10

17) 1 cm = _____ mm   C) 1

18) 1 dL = _____ mL   D) 0.001

19) 1 mL = _____ cc   E) 1000

20) 1 kg = _____ g

15) D   16) E   17) B   18) A   19) C   20) E

Chapter 2 Energy and Matter

2.1 Multiple-Choice Questions

1) An example of kinetic energy is
    A) a coiled spring.
    B) running water.
    C) a tree.
    D) natural gas.
    E) chemical energy.
  Answer: B

2) The energy associated with the motion of particles in a substance is called
    A) temperature.
    B) electrical energy.
    C) heat.
    D) chemical energy.
    E) potential energy.
  Answer: C

3) Which of the following is an example of potential energy?
    A) chewing food
    B) water stored in a reservoir
    C) burning wood
    D) a fan blade turning
    E) riding an exercise bike
  Answer: B

4) The phrase "ability to do work" is a definition of
    A) specific heat.
    B) energy.
    C) calorie.
    D) heating.
    E) cooling.
  Answer: B

5) The energy stored in chemical bonds is
    A) specific heat.
    B) kinetic energy.
    C) potential energy.
    D) work.
    E) a calorie.
  Answer: C

6) The energy of motion is referred to as
   A) work.
   B) freezing.
   C) specific heat.
   D) potential energy.
   E) kinetic energy.

Answer: E

7) Global warming is believed to result from all of the following except
   A) burning of fossil fuels.
   B) increasing levels of carbon dioxide in the atmosphere.
   C) deforestation.
   D) movement of the earth closer to the sun.
   E) carbon dioxide trapping the heat produced by the sun.

Answer: D

8) In which of the following would the particles move most rapidly?
   A) ice at –20 °C
   B) water at 20 °C
   C) steam at 110 °C
   D) boiling water
   E) ice at 0 °C

Answer: C

9) 650. J is the same amount of energy as

   A) 155 cal   B) 2720 cal   C) 650 cal   D) 1550 cal   E) 2.72 cal

Answer: A

10) 3.25 kcal is the same amount of energy as
    A) 3.25 J   B) 0.777 J   C) 777 J   D) 13600 J   E) 13.6 J

Answer: D

11) A potato contains 20 g of carbohydrate. If carbohydrate has a caloric value of 4 kcal/g, how many kcal are obtained from the carbohydrate in the potato?
    A) 5 kcal   B) 20 kcal   C) 40 kcal   D) 60 kcal   E) 80 kcal

Answer: E

12) One cup of kidney beans contains 15 g of protein, 1 g of fat, and 42 g of carbohydrate. How many kilocalories, to two significant figures, does this sample contain? (The caloric values are: 4 kcal/g for carbohydrate, 9 kcal/g for fat, and 4 kcal/g for protein.)
    A) 60 kcal   B) 88 kcal   C) 230 kcal   D) 240 kcal   E) 520 kcal

Answer: D

13) A cheeseburger from a fast food restaurant contains 19 g of fat, 20 g of carbohydrate, and 28 g of protein. How many kcal of energy does the cheeseburger contain? (The caloric values are: 4 kcal/g for carbohydrate, 9 kcal/g for fat, and 4 kcal/g for protein.) Report the answer to 2 significant figures.
    A) 70. kcal   B) 360 kcal   C) 17 kcal   D) 630 kcal   E) 280 kcal

Answer: B

14) A serving of fish contains 50 g protein and 4 g of fat. If protein has a caloric value of 4 kcal/g and fat has 9 kcal/g, how many kcal are in the serving? Give the answer to 2 significant figures.
    A) 240 kcal   B) 54 kcal   C) 470 kcal   D) 220 kcal   E) 490 kcal
    Answer: A

15) A slice of pizza contains 28g of carbohydrate, 13g of protein and fat. If the pizza contains 280 kcal, how many grams of fat are present?(The caloric values are: 4 kcal/g for carbohydrate, 9 kcal/g for fat, and 4 kcal/g for protein.)
    A) 28 g   B) 13 g   C) 10. g   D) 55 g   E) 250 g
    Answer: B

16) The dietary calorie(Cal) is equal to
    A) 1000 kilocalories.
    B) 1000 calories.
    C) 100 calories.
    D) 10 calories.
    E) 1 calorie.
    Answer: B

17) A temperature of 41 °F is the same as
    A) 5 °C.   B) 310 °C.   C) –9 °C.   D) 16 °C.   E) 42 °C.
    Answer: A

18) If the temperature is 20. °C, what is the corresponding temperature on the Fahrenheit scale?
    A) –22 °F   B) 68 °F   C) 43 °F   D) 239 °F   E) 94 °F
    Answer: B

19) If the temperature is –55 °F, what is the corresponding temperature on the Kelvin scale?
    A) 225 K   B) 218 K   C) 55 K   D) 273 K   E) 328 K
    Answer: A

20) A patient has a temperature of 38.5 °C. What is the temperature in degrees Fahrenheit?
    A) 70.5 °F   B) 311 °F   C) 126.9 °F   D) 101.3 °F   E) 11.7 °F
    Answer: D

21) The temperature of liquid nitrogen is –196 °C. What is the corresponding reading on the Kelvin scale?
    A) 77 K   B) –127 K   C) –91 K   D) 48 K   E) 146 K
    Answer: A

22) On a hot day, the thermometer read 95°F. What is the temperature in degrees Celsius?
    A) 77 °C   B) 113 °C   C) 35 °C   D) 63 °C   E) 178 °C
    Answer: C

23) Absolute zero is
    A) the freezing point of water using the Celsius scale.
    B) the boiling point of liquid nitrogen.
    C) the temperature on the Kelvin scale corresponding to 32 °F.
    D) the coldest temperature possible.
    E) the freezing point of liquid nitrogen.
    Answer: D

24) The specific heat of a substance is the amount of heat needed to
    A) change 1 g of the substance from the solid to the liquid state.
    B) raise the temperature of 1 g of the substance by 1 °C.
    C) change 1 g of the substance from the liquid to the solid state.
    D) convert 1 g of a liquid to gas.
    E) convert 1 g of a solid to a gas.

Answer: B

25) A kilocalorie of heat is required to raise the temperature of
    A) 1 g of water from 14 °C to 15 °C.
    B) 1 g of water by 10 °C.
    C) 10 g of water by 10 °C.
    D) 100 g of water by 10 °C.
    E) 100 g of water by 100 °C.

Answer: D

26) How many calories are required to raise the temperature of a 35.0 g sample of iron from 25 °C
    to 35 °C? Iron has a specific heat of 0.108 cal/g °C.
    A) 38 cal   B) 1.1 cal   C) 3.8cal   D) 93 cal   E) 130 cal

Answer: A

27) How many calories are required to raise the temperature of a 150. g sample of gold from 25 °C
    to 175 °C? The specific heat of gold is 0.0308 cal/g °C.
    A) 4.62 cal   B) 116 cal   C) 22500 cal   D) 693 cal   E) 130 cal

Answer: D

28) How many calories are required to increase the temperature of 13 g of alcohol from 11 °C to 23
    °C? The specific heat of alcohol is 0.59 cal/g °C.
    A) 83 cal   B) 0.63 cal   C) 92 cal   D) 0.54 cal   E) 170 cal

Answer: C

29) The specific heat of copper is 0.093cal/g °C, and the specific heat of silver is 0.057 cal/g °C. If 100
    cal of heat is added to one g of each metal at 25 °C, what is the expected result?
    A) The copper will reach a higher temperature.
    B) The silver will reach a higher temperature.
    C) The two samples will reach the same temperature.
    D) The copper will reach a temperature lower than 25 °C.
    E) The silver will soften.

Answer: B

30) Which of the following quantities is NOT required to calculate the amount of heat energy
    required to heat water from 25 °C to 55 °C?
    A) the mass of the water sample
    B) the initial temperature
    C) the final temperature
    D) the specific heat of water
    E) the heat of vaporization for water

Answer: E

31) Raising the temperature of 10.0 g of water from 10.0 °C to 20.0 °C requires 100.0 cal of energy, while raising the temperature of 10.0 g of aluminum from 10.0 °C to 20.0 °C requires 22 cal. More calories are required to heat the water because
    A) water is a liquid and aluminum is a solid at 10.0 °C.
    B) ten grams of water occupies a larger volume than 10.0 g of aluminum.
    C) water has a greater potential energy than aluminum.
    D) water has a larger specific heat than aluminum.
    E) 10.0 °C is closer to the melting point of water than to the melting point of aluminum.
    Answer: D

32) The number of calories needed to raise the temperature of 32 g of water from 12 °C to 54 °C is
    A) 384 cal.   B) 1.3 cal.   C) 1300 cal.   D) 1700 cal.   E) 0.76 cal.
    Answer: C

33) Which of the following is a property of a solid?
    A) It takes the shape of the container.
    B) It fills the volume of the container.
    C) The particles move at a rapid rate.
    D) The interactions between its particles are very weak.
    E) The particles have fixed positions and are very close together.
    Answer: E

34) In a gas, the distance between the particles is
    A) very close relative to the size of the molecules.
    B) close relative to the size of the molecules.
    C) fixed relative to the size of the molecules.
    D) small relative to the size of the molecules.
    E) very large relative to the size of the molecules.
    Answer: E

35) Which of the following is a physical property of both liquids and gases?
    A) has its own shape
    B) has a definite volume
    C) has strong interactions between its particles
    D) has randomly arranged particles
    E) has large spaces between molecules
    Answer: D

36) Which one of the following properties describes a liquid?
    A) has its own shape
    B) particles are close together and move randomly
    C) particles move very rapidly
    D) fills the entire volume of the container
    E) There is essentially no interaction between the particles.
    Answer: B

37) The physical state(s) present when a substance is melting is (are)
   A) solid.
   B) liquid.
   C) gas.
   D) solid + liquid.
   E) liquid + gas.

Answer: D

38) If the heat of fusion for water is 80. cal/g, how many calories are needed to melt 45.0 g of ice at 0 °C?
   A) 3.6 cal
   B) 3.6×10^3 cal
   C) 1.8 cal
   D) 80. cal
   E) 0.56 cal

Answer: B

39) The formation of a gas resulting from the escape of high–energy particles from the surface of a liquid is known as
   A) evaporation.
   B) deposition.
   C) boiling.
   D) melting.
   E) sublimation.

Answer: A

40) When a solid is converted directly to a gas, the change of state is called
   A) freezing.
   B) melting.
   C) boiling.
   D) condensation.
   E) sublimation.

Answer: E

41) A burn from steam at 100°C is expected to be more severe than a burn from boiling water at 100°C because
   A) the steam is hotter than the boiling water.
   B) there is more steam than water.
   C) the steam will give off a large amount of heat as it condenses.
   D) you are more likely to come into contact with the steam than with the boiling water.
   E) All of these answers are correct.

Answer: C

42) The heat of fusion for water is 80. cal/g. How many calories of heat are released when 20.0 g of water at 0 °C is frozen to ice?
   A) 600 cal   B) 1600 cal   C) 2000 cal   D) 2200 cal   E) 0 cal

Answer: B

43) The heat of fusion for water is 80. cal/g. How many calories of heat are needed to melt a 35 g ice cube that has a temperature of 0 °C?

   A) 2300 cal   B) 1600 cal   C) 2800 cal   D) 540 cal   E) 0 cal

   Answer: C

44) The heat of vaporization for water is 540 cal/g. How many kilocalories are needed to change 22 g of liquid water to steam at 100 °C?

   A) 540 kcal
   B) 12 kcal
   C) 12000 kcal
   D) 25 kcal
   E) 1.8 kcal

   Answer: B

45) If the heat of vaporization for water is 540 cal/g, how many kilocalories are released when 5.00 g of steam is converted to liquid at 100 °C?

   A) 540 kcal   B) 5.0 kcal   C) 110 kcal   D) 2.7 kcal   E) 5.4 kcal

   Answer: D

46) Which of the following does NOT involve a change of state?

   A) melting ice
   B) freezing water
   C) vaporization of alcohol
   D) sublimation of dry ice
   E) pouring water into a vacuum-insulated bottle

   Answer: E

47) A heating curve illustrates

   A) what a substance looks like as it is heated.
   B) what happens to the particles of a substance as it is heated.
   C) what happens to the heat applied as the temperature is increased.
   D) the changes in the temperature and physical state of a substance as it is heated.
   E) the chemical changes that occur as the substance is heated.

   Answer: D

48) On a heating curve a plateau corresponds to

   A) a change in temperature of a liquid.
   B) a change in temperature of a solid.
   C) a change in temperature of a gas.
   D) a change of state.
   E) the solid being broken into smaller pieces.

   Answer: D

49) Which of the following does NOT represent a step on the heating curve of water?

   A) The temperature of steam cannot exceed 100 °C.
   B) The temperature of ice remains at 0 °C as it melts.
   C) The temperature of liquid water increases linearly as it is heated.
   D) The temperature of liquid water remains at 100 °C as it boils.
   E) Both liquid water and ice are present at 0 °C.

   Answer: A

2.2 Short Answer Questions

1) The change of state from solid to gas is termed _____.

Answer: sublimation

2) The heat of fusion is the amount of heat necessary to change one gram of a substance from the solid to the _____ state.

Answer: liquid

3) The amount of heat necessary for one gram of a substance to change from the solid state to the liquid state is the _____.

Answer: heat of fusion

4) When a liquid boils, the process by which the molecules leave its surface is called _____.

Answer: evaporation

Bromine (Br_2) has a freezing point of –7 °C, and a boiling point of 60 °C.
Indicate the state or change of state occurring at each temperature.

5) 30 °C

Answer: liquid

6) 60 °C

Answer: boiling

7) –7 °C

Answer: melting

8) –15 °C

Answer: solid

9) 70 °C

Answer: gas

2.3 True/False Questions

1) As heat is removed from a solid, its temperature decreases.

Answer: TRUE

2) Water vapor is a gas.

Answer: TRUE

3) When a liquid is boiling, its temperature does not change.

Answer: TRUE

4) As a solid melts, its temperature does not change.

Answer: TRUE

5) Steam at 100 °C holds the same amount of heat as water at 100 °C.

Answer: FALSE

6) The temperature at which water melts and freezes is the same.

Answer: TRUE

7) Water freezes at 100 °C.
   Answer: FALSE

8) The heat of fusion of water is larger thatn the heat of vaporization.
   Answer: FALSE

9) Carbohydrates and proteins have the same caloric value per gram.
   Answer: TRUE

10) Condensation occurs when a liquid is converted to a solid.
    Answer: FALSE

2.4 Matching Questions

Identify the physical state(s) corresponding to labeled regions on the cooling curve of water shown below.

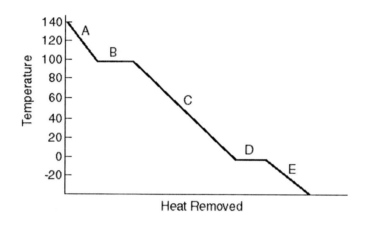

1) Region A	A) liquid
2) Region B	B) solid and gas
3) Region C	C) solid
4) Region D	D) liquid and solid
5) Region E	E) liquid and gas
	F) gas

1) F   2) E   3) A   4) D   5) C

Match the state of matter with each of the following descriptions of a substance.

6) Particles are held close together in a random pattern.

A) solid

B) solid + liquid

7) Great distances exist between the particles.

C) gas

8) This material has a definite volume, and a definite shape.

D) liquid + gas

E) liquid

9) This substance is boiling.

10) This substance is melting.

6) E   7) C   8) A   9) D   10) B

Chapter 3 Atoms and Elements

3.1 Multiple-Choice Questions

1) Helium is a(n)
    A) compound.
    B) heterogeneous mixture.
    C) element.
    D) homogeneous mixture.
    E) electron.

    Answer: C

2) Air is a(n)
    A) compound.
    B) heterogeneous mixture.
    C) element.
    D) homogeneous mixture.
    E) none of the above

    Answer: D

3) Coins in a piggy bank is a(n)
    A) compound.
    B) heterogeneous mixture.
    C) element.
    D) homogeneous mixture.
    E) none of the above

    Answer: B

4) Gold in a ring is a(n)
    A) compound.
    B) heterogeneous mixture.
    C) element.
    D) homogeneous mixture.
    E) none of the above

    Answer: C

5) The primary substances of which all other things are composed are
    A) molecules.
    B) compounds.
    C) elements.
    D) electrons.
    E) protons.

    Answer: C

6) Au is the symbol for
   A) gold.
   B) silver.
   C) argon.
   D) aluminum.
   E) sodium.
   Answer: A

Select the correct symbol for the element named.
7) aluminum
   A) Al   B) Am   C) Au   D) Sn   E) Ag
   Answer: A

8) iron
   A) Ir   B) Fs   C) Fe   D) In   E) FE
   Answer: C

9) sodium
   A) So   B) Na   C) No   D) Sm   E) Au
   Answer: B

10) mercury
    A) Mr   B) Na   C) Au   D) Hg   E) Au
    Answer: D

11) potassium
    A) P   B) Po   C) Pt   D) K   E) Ko
    Answer: D

12) silver
    A) S   B) Si   C) Ag   D) Au   E) AG
    Answer: C

13) Ca is the symbol for
    A) calcium.
    B) carbon.
    C) cobalt.
    D) copper.
    E) cadmium.
    Answer: A

14) What elements are in hydroxyapatite, $Ca_5(PO_4)_3OH$, a major compound in human bones and teeth?
    A) carbon, potassium, oxygen, hydrogen
    B) calcium, phosphorous, oxygen, hydrogen
    C) carbon, phosphorous, oxygen, helium
    D) calcium, phosphorous, oxygen, helium
    E) carbon, potassium, oxygen, helium
    Answer: B

15) Which of the following is a characteristic of the modern periodic table?
    A) A group is a horizontal row on the periodic table.
    B) A period is a column on the periodic table.
    C) The elements in each group have similar chemical properties.
    D) The B groups contain the representative elements.
    E) The A groups contain the transition elements.

Answer: C

16) Which of the following properties is NOT a characteristic of the Group 1A(1) elements (alkali metals)?
    A) They are shiny.
    B) They are good conductors of heat.
    C) They react vigorously with water.
    D) Most of them are liquids at room temperature.
    E) They are good conductors of electricity.

Answer: D

17) The Group 8A(18) elements
    A) are unreactive and are rarely found in combination with other elements.
    B) are good conductors of electricity.
    C) melt at high temperatures.
    D) are liquids at room temperature.
    E) react vigorously with water.

Answer: A

18) Which of the following elements is a metal?
    A) nitrogen
    B) fluorine
    C) argon
    D) strontium
    E) phosphorus

Answer: D

19) Which of the following elements is a nonmetal?
    A) nitrogen   B) sodium   C) iron   D) silver   E) calcium

Answer: A

20) Which of the following is a characteristic of nonmetals?
    A) shiny
    B) malleable
    C) good conductors of heat
    D) low melting points
    E) good conductors of electricity

Answer: D

21) Which of the following elements is a noble gas?
    A) oxygen   B) chlorine   C) bromine   D) argon   E) nitrogen

Answer: D

22) The smallest particle of an element that retains the characteristics of the element is a(n)
    A) electron.   B) neutron.   C) proton.   D) atom.   E) nucleus.

Answer: D

23) According to the Atomic Theory,
    A) all atoms are different.
    B) atoms are neither created nor destroyed during a chemical reaction.
    C) atoms of the same element combine to form compounds.
    D) all matter is made up of tiny particles called electrons.
    E) a compound can contain different numbers of atoms as long as it has the same kinds of atoms.

Answer: B

24) Which of the following descriptions of a subatomic particle is correct?
    A) A proton has a positive charge and a mass of approximately 1 amu.
    B) An electron has a negative charge and a mass of approximately 1 amu.
    C) A neutron has no charge and its mass is negligible.
    D) A proton has a positive charge and a negligible mass.
    E) A neutron has a positive charge and a mass of approximately 1 amu.

Answer: A

25) In an atom, the nucleus contains
    A) an equal number of protons and electrons.
    B) all the protons and neutrons.
    C) all the protons and electrons.
    D) only neutrons.
    E) only protons.

Answer: B

26) The atomic number of an atom is equal to the number of
    A) nuclei.
    B) neutrons.
    C) neutrons plus protons.
    D) electrons plus protons.
    E) protons.

Answer: E

27) The number of neutrons in an atom is equal to
    A) the atomic number.
    B) the mass number.
    C) the mass number + the atomic number.
    D) the mass number – the atomic number.
    E) the number of protons.

Answer: D

28) The mass number of an atom can be calculated from
    A) the number of electrons.
    B) the number of protons plus neutrons.
    C) the number of protons.
    D) the number of electrons plus protons.
    E) the number of neutrons.

Answer: B

29) What is the mass number of an atom of potassium that has 20 neutrons?
    A) 15   B) 19   C) 35   D) 39   E) 59

Answer: D

30) Consider a neutral atom with 30 protons and 34 neutrons. The atomic number of the element is
    A) 30.   B) 32.   C) 34.   D) 64.   E) 94.

Answer: A

31) Consider a neutral atom with 30 protons and 34 neutrons. The mass number for this atom is
    A) 30.   B) 32.   C) 34.   D) 64.   E) 94.

Answer: D

32) Consider a neutral atom with 30 protons and 34 neutrons. The number of electrons in this atom
    is
    A) 30.   B) 32.   C) 34.   D) 64.   E) 94.

Answer: A

33) How many protons are in an isotope of sodium with a mass number of 25?
    A) 11   B) 14   C) 15   D) 25   E) 32

Answer: A

34) Consider an isotope of sodium with a mass number of 25. The number of neutrons in this
    isotope of sodium is
    A) 11.   B) 14.   C) 16.   D) 25.   E) 32.

Answer: B

35) Which of the following gives the correct numbers of protons, neutrons, and electrons in a
    neutral atom of $^{118}_{50}$Sn?

    A) 118 protons, 50 neutrons, 118 electrons
    B) 118 protons, 118 neutrons, 50 electrons
    C) 50 protons, 68 neutrons, 50 electrons
    D) 68 protons, 68 neutrons, 50 electrons
    E) 50 protons, 50 neutrons, 50 electrons

Answer: C

36) Isotopes are atoms of the same element that have
    A) different atomic numbers.
    B) the same atomic numbers but different numbers of protons.
    C) the same atomic numbers but different numbers of electrons.
    D) the same atomic number but different numbers of neutrons.
    E) the same atomic mass but different numbers of protons.

Answer: D

37) The correct symbol for the isotope of potassium with 22 neutrons is

A) $^{41}_{19}$K.   B) $^{19}_{41}$K.   C) $^{37}_{15}$P.   D) $^{15}_{37}$P.   E) $^{22}_{19}$K.

Answer: A

38) The atomic mass of an element is equal to
    A) its mass number.
    B) its atomic number.
    C) one–twelfth of the mass of a carbon–12 atom.
    D) the mass of an average atom.
    E) the mass of the heaviest isotope.

Answer: D

39) A sample of chlorine has two naturally occurring isotopes. The isotope Cl–35 makes up 75.8% of the sample, and the isotope Cl–37 makes up 24.3% of the sample. Which of the following statements is true?
    A) The atomic mass of chlorine will be less than 35.
    B) The atomic mass of chlorine will be more than 37.
    C) You cannot tell what the atomic mass will be.
    D) The atomic mass will be between 35 and 37.
    E) The atomic mass will be 24.3.

Answer: D

40) Which of the following is NOT true for the atoms ^{13}N, ^{14}N, and ^{15}N?
    A) They all have the same mass number.
    B) They are isotopes.
    C) They all have the same atomic number.
    D) They all have 7 protons.
    E) They all have 7 electrons.

Answer: A

41) The elements lithium, sodium, and potassium
    A) are isotopes of each other.
    B) are in the same period of elements.
    C) have the same number of neutrons.
    D) are in the same group.
    E) have the same mass number.

Answer: D

42) The elements sodium, magnesium,and silicon
    A) are isotopes of each other.
    B) are in the same period of elements.
    C) have the same number of neutrons.
    D) are in the same group.
    E) have the same mass number.

Answer: B

43) The electron arrangement of any particular atom shows
   A) the number of isotopes possible.
   B) a description of the shape of each electron energy level.
   C) the number of electrons in each energy level.
   D) a diagram of an atomic nucleus.
   E) the maximum number of electrons each energy level can hold.
   Answer: C

44) The maximum number of electrons that may occupy the third electron energy level is
   A) 2.   B) 8.   C) 10.   D) 18.   E) 32.
   Answer: D

45) What is the element with the electron arrangement 2,8,7?
   A) Be   B) Cl   C) F   D) S   E) Ar
   Answer: B

46) What is the electron energy level arrangement for aluminum?
   A) 2,8,3   B) 2,8,5   C) 2,8,7   D) 2,8,8   E) 2,8,10
   Answer: A

47) What is the electron energy level arrangement for potassium (atomic number 19)?
   A) 2,8,9   B) 2,8,7,2   C) 2,10,7   D) 2,8,8,1   E) 2,8,6,3
   Answer: D

48) What element has the electron energy level arrangement 2,8,4?
   A) carbon   B) oxygen   C) sulfur   D) iron   E) silicon
   Answer: E

49) The number of electrons in the outer energy level of a neutral atom of boron (atomic number 5) is
   A) 2.   B) 3.   C) 5.   D) 8.   E) 10.
   Answer: B

50) Which element would have physical and chemical properties similar to chlorine?
   A) Ar   B) Br   C) S   D) O   E) P
   Answer: B

51) What is the symbol of the element in Group 4A(14) and Period 2?
   A) Be   B) Mg   C) Ca   D) C   E) Si
   Answer: D

52) What is the correct electron arrangement for the lithium atom?
   A) 3   B) 3,1   C) 1,2   D) 2,1   E) 2,5
   Answer: D

53) The number of electron energy levels in a magnesium atom is
   A) 1.   B) 2.   C) 3.   D) 4.   E) 5.
   Answer: C

54) The element in this list with chemical properties similar to magnesium is
  A) sodium.
  B) boron.
  C) carbon.
  D) strontium.
  E) chlorine.
  Answer: D

55) Identify the noble gas in the following list.
  A) helium   B) nitrogen   C) oxygen   D) gold   E) chlorine
  Answer: A

56) Semiconductors are located in the periodic table on (or in) the
  A) left side of the table.
  B) right side of the table.
  C) line dividing metals from nonmetals in the table.
  D) first period of the table.
  E) last period of the table.
  Answer: C

57) Identify the metalloid in the following list.
  A) sulfur
  B) fluorine
  C) silver
  D) copper
  E) germanium
  Answer: E

58) The number of valence electrons found in an atom of a Group A element is equal to
  A) its atomic number.
  B) its mass number.
  C) its group number.
  D) eight.
  E) eight minus the group number.
  Answer: C

59) Valence electrons are electrons located
  A) in the outermost energy level of an atom.
  B) in the nucleus of an atom.
  C) in the innermost energy level of an atom.
  D) throughout the atom.
  E) in the first three shells of an atom.
  Answer: A

60) In an electron–dot structure of an element, the dots are used to represent
  A) all of the electrons in the atom.
  B) the valence electrons.
  C) the electron arrangement.
  D) only the electrons that will participate in bond formation.
  E) the electrons that the element will gain when it forms a compound.
  Answer: B

61) How many valence electrons are in the electron-dot structures for the elements in group 3A(13)?

   A) 1   B) 2   C) 3   D) 4   E) 6

   Answer: C

62) The number of dots in the electron dot structure of nitrogen is

   A) one.   B) two.   C) three.   D) four.   E) five.

   Answer: E

63) The number of dots in the electron dot structure of carbon is

   A) one.   B) two.   C) three.   D) four.   E) five.

   Answer: D

64) Which of the following is the correct electron-dot structure for carbon?

   A)   B)   C)   D)   E)

   Answer: C

65) The atomic size of atoms

   A) increases going across a period.
   B) decreases going across a period.
   C) decreases going down within a group.
   D) does not change going across a period.
   E) none of the above

   Answer: B

66) The atomic size of atoms

   A) increases going across a period.
   B) decreases going down within a group.
   C) increases going down within a group.
   D) does not change going down within a group.
   E) none of the above

   Answer: C

67) The ionization energy of atoms

   A) decreases going across a period.
   B) decreases going down within a group.
   C) increases going down within a group.
   D) does not change going down within a group.
   E) none of the above

   Answer: B

68) Ionization energy is

   A) the energy an ion acquires from an electron.
   B) the energy needed to remove the least tightly bound electron.
   C) highest for metals in Group 1A(1).
   D) higher for potassiun than for lithium.
   E) none of the above

   Answer: B

36

3.2 Short Answer Questions

Write the electron energy level arrangement for the atom shown.

   1) Sodium

      Answer: 2,8,1

   2) Chlorine

      Answer: 2,8,7

   3) Argon

      Answer: 2,8,8

   4) Sulfur

      Answer: 2,8,6

   5) Magnesium

      Answer: 2,8,2

   6) Phosphorus

      Answer: 2,8,5

3.3 True/False Questions

   1) Sulfur is a non-metal.

      Answer: TRUE

   2) Ionization enrgy increases going down a group.

      Answer: FALSE

   3) Atomic size decreases going from left to right within a period.

      Answer: TRUE

   4) Iodine is a metal.

      Answer: FALSE

   5) Sulfur has 16 valence electrons.

      Answer: FALSE

   6) Potassium has one valence electron.

      Answer: TRUE

   7) The symbol for potassium his P.

      Answer: FALSE

   8) Chromium is a metal.

      Answer: TRUE

   9) Radon is a metal.

      Answer: FALSE

   10) Mercury is a metal.

      Answer: TRUE

3.4 Matching Questions

Do the following represent elements in a group, a period, or neither?

    1) Li, Na, K   A) group

    2) Li, C, F   B) neither

    3) F, S, P   C) period

    4) O, S, Se

    5) He, H, I

1) A   2) C   3) B   4) A   5) B

Match the correct symbols with the names of elements.

    6) calcium   A) Ca

    7) copper   B) Cu

    8) carbon   C) Co

    9) chlorine   D) Cl

    10) cobalt   E) C

6) A   7) B   8) E   9) D   10) C

Give the correct number of electrons.

    11) in the outer energy level of   A) seven
         nitrogen

                                        B) one

    12) in the second energy level of
         magnesium   C) five

    13) in the highest occupied   D) two
         electron energy level of
         chlorine   E) eight

    14) in the first electron energy
         level of chlorine

    15) in the third energy level of
         sodium

11) C   12) E   13) A   14) D   15) B

Classify the following elements.

16) sodium   A) alkali metal

17) argon   B) halogen

18) bromine   C) noble gas

19) copper   D) alkaline earth metal

20) magnesium   E) transition element

16) A   17) C   18) B   19) E   20) D

Classify the following elements as metals or nonmetals.

21) phosphorus   A) nonmetal

22) chlorine   B) metal

23) cobalt

24) sulfur

25) nickel

21) A   22) A   23) B   24) A   25) B

Chapter 4 Compounds and Their Bonds

4.1 Multiple-Choice Questions

1) The octet rule indicates that
  A) all of the noble gases have eight total electrons.
  B) all of the shells in an atom hold a maximum of 8 electrons.
  C) all of the Group A elements have 8 valence electrons.
  D) atoms lose, gain, or share valence electrons to have 8 valence electrons.
  E) the noble gases react with other compounds to get 8 valence electrons.

Answer: D

2) In ionic compounds, _____ lose their valence electrons to form positively charged _____.
  A) metals, anions
  B) nonmetals, cations
  C) metals, polyatomic ions
  D) nonmetals, anions
  E) metals, cations

Answer: E

3) How many electrons will aluminum gain or lose when it forms an ion?
  A) lose 1   B) gain 5   C) lose 2   D) lose 3   E) gain 1

Answer: D

4) What is the symbol for the ion with 19 protons and 18 electrons?
  A) F^+ B) F^- C) Ar^+ D) K^- E) K^+

Answer: E

5) To form an ion, a sodium atom
  A) gains one electron.
  B) gains two electrons.
  C) loses seven electrons.
  D) loses one electron.
  E) loses two electrons.

Answer: D

6) An anion always
  A) has a positive charge.
  B) contains a group of two or more atoms with a positive charge.
  C) contains a metal and a nonmetal.
  D) forms covalent bonds.
  E) has a negative charge.

Answer: E

7) What is the ionic charge of an ion with 18 protons and 15 electrons?
  A) 1^+ B) 2^+ C) 3^+ D) 2^- E) 3^-

Answer: C

8) The number of electrons in an ion with 20 protons and an ionic charge of 2⁻ is
   A) 24.   B) 22.   C) 20.   D) 18.   E) 16.

   Answer: B

9) Elements in group 2A(2) of the periodic table form ions with a charge of
   A) 1⁺.   B) 1⁻.   C) 2⁺.   D) 3⁺.   E) 0.

   Answer: C

10) The ion of aluminum is
   A) Al^+.   B) Al^{2+}.   C) Al^{3+}.   D) Al^{3-}.   E) Al^{2-}.

   Answer: C

11) How many electrons will chlorine gain or lose when it forms an ion?
   A) lose 1   B) gain 1   C) lose 7   D) gain 2   E) lose 3

   Answer: B

12) An ionic compound
   A) has a net positive charge.
   B) has a net negative charge.
   C) contains only cations.
   D) contains only anions.
   E) has a net charge of zero.

   Answer: E

13) The correct formula for a compound formed from the elements Al and O is
   A) AlO.   B) Al_2O.   C) Al_3O_2.   D) AlO_3.   E) Al_2O_3.

   Answer: E

14) The correct formula for the compound formed from Mg and S is
   A) MgS.   B) MgS_2.   C) Mg_2S.   D) Mg_2S_2.   E) Mg_2S_3.

   Answer: A

15) Which one of the following compounds contains an ion with a 3+ charge?
   A) KCl   B) Na_2O C) $FeCl_3$ D) CuCl   E) $MgCl_2$

   Answer: C

16) What is the correct formula for the oxide ion?
   A) O^{2-} B) O   C) O^+ D) O^{2+} E) O^{3+}

   Answer: A

17) The compound $MgCl_2$ is named
   A) magnesium chlorine.
   B) magnesium dichloride.
   C) magnesium (II) chloride.
   D) magnesium chloride.
   E) dimagnesium chloride.

   Answer: D

18) Which one of the following elements forms two or more ions with different ionic charges?

    A) K   B) F   C) Ca   D) O   E) Fe

Answer: E

19) What is the correct formula for the iron (II) ion?

    A) Fe^+ B) Fe^{2+} C) Fe^{3+} D) Fe^{2-} E) Fe^{3-}

Answer: B

20) The name of the Cu^+ ion is

    A) copper (II).
    B) copper (I).
    C) copper (III).
    D) copper.
    E) cuprum.

Answer: B

21) What is the correct formula for iron (III) sulfide?

    A) Fe_2S_2 B) Fe_2S C) FeS D) FeS_2 E) Fe_2S_3

Answer: E

22) A(n) _____ is the smallest neutral unit of two or more atoms held together by a covalent bond.

    A) ionic compound
    B) nucleus
    C) molecule
    D) formula
    E) unit

Answer: C

23) In a molecule with covalent bonding,

    A) oppositely charged ions are held together by strong electrical attractions.
    B) atoms of metals form bonds to atoms of nonmetals.
    C) atoms of different metals form bonds.
    D) atoms are held together by sharing electrons.
    E) atoms of noble gases are held together by attractions between oppositely charged ions.

Answer: D

24) Which of the following elements does NOT exist as a diatomic molecule?

    A) hydrogen   B) nitrogen   C) chlorine   D) oxygen   E) carbon

Answer: E

25) In a covalently bonded molecule, the number of electrons that an atom shares with others is usually equal to the number of electrons

    A) in the atom.
    B) in its nucleus.
    C) in all the atoms.
    D) in its ion.
    E) needed to give it a noble gas arrangement.

Answer: E

26) Double and triple bonds form because
    A) the atoms involved have high electronegativities.
    B) single covalent bonds do not give all of the atoms in the molecule eight valence electrons.
    C) one of the atoms in the molecule has more than 8 valence electrons.
    D) the ions involved have charges larger than one.
    E) there is at least one hydrogen atom involved in the bond.
    Answer: B

27) The correct name of the compound NCl_3 is
    A) nitrogen chloride.
    B) trinitrogen chloride
    C) nitrogen(III) chloride.
    D) nickel chloride.
    E) nitrogen trichloride.
    Answer: E

28) According to naming rules, the types of compound that use prefixes in their names are
    A) ionic compounds.
    B) ionic compounds involving transition metals.
    C) polyatomic ions.
    D) covalent compounds.
    E) compounds that contain polyatomic ions.
    Answer: D

29) The correct name for the compound N_2O_3 is
    A) nitrogen oxide.
    B) nitrogen trioxide.
    C) dinitride trioxide.
    D) dinitrogen oxide.
    E) dinitrogen trioxide.
    Answer: E

30) What is the formula of carbon tetraiodide?
    A) CI   B) CI_4 C) C_4I D) CI_3 E) C_2I_4
    Answer: B

31) The name of $Al_2(SO_4)_3$ is
    A) aluminum(III) sulfate.
    B) dialuminum trisulfate.
    C) dialuminum sulfate.
    D) dialuminum trisulfide.
    E) aluminum sulfate.
    Answer: E

32) The ability of an atom to attract the shared electrons in a covalent bond is its
    A) electronegativity.
    B) bonding ability.
    C) polarity.
    D) ionic character.
    E) nonpolarity.

Answer: A

33) Which of the following substances contains a nonpolar covalent bond?
    A) H_2O B) NaCl   C) NH_3 D) MgF_2 E) N_2

Answer: E

34) Which of the following compounds contains a polar covalent bond?
    A) NaF   B) HCl   C) Br_2 D) MgO   E) O_2

Answer: B

35) Which of the following compounds contains an ionic bond?
    A) NH_3 B) H_2O C) CaO   D) H_2 E) CH_4

Answer: C

36) Ionic bonding is expected in which of these compounds?
    A) Cl_2 B) KF   C) OF_2 D) HF   E) H_2

Answer: B

37) A polar covalent bond is found in which of these compounds?
    A) H_2O B) F_2 C) NaCl   D) H_2 E) N_2

Answer: A

38) The bond in Cl_2 is a(n)
    A) ionic bond.
    B) nonpolar covalent bond.
    C) metallic bond.
    D) polar ionic bond.
    E) no bond.

Answer: B

39) A group of covalently bonded atoms that has an overall electrical charge is called a(n)
    A) ionic compound.
    B) anion.
    C) polyatomic ion.
    D) cation.
    E) molecule.

Answer: C

40) Which of the following polyatomic ions has a positive charge?
   A) hydroxide
   B) cyanide
   C) hydrogen carbonate
   D) ammonium
   E) nitrate

Answer: D

41) Which of the following polyatomic ions has a 3- ionic charge?
   A) hydroxide
   B) nitrate
   C) sulfate
   D) phosphate
   E) hydrogen carbonate

Answer: D

42) What is the formula of the nitride ion?

   A) N^{3-} B) NO_2^- C) NO_3^{3-} D) NO_3^{2-} E) NO_3^-

Answer: A

43) The name of the HSO_4^- ion is

   A) sulfate.
   B) hydrogen sulfate.
   C) sulfite.
   D) hydrogen sulfite.
   E) sulfide.

Answer: B

44) What is the formula of a compound that contains Na^+ and PO_4^{3-} ions?

   A) Na_3PO_4 B) $NaPO_4$ C) Na_2PO_3 D) Na_3PO_3 E) Na_3P

Answer: A

45) $Fe_2(SO_4)_3$ is called
   A) iron sulfate.
   B) iron (II) sulfate.
   C) iron (III) sulfate.
   D) diiron trisulfate.
   E) iron trisulfate.

Answer: C

46) What is the formula for aluminum nitrate?
  A) Al_2NO_2
  B) $AlNO_3$
  C) $Al(NO_2)_3$
  D) $Al(NO_3)_3$
  E) $Al_2(NO_2)_2$

Answer: D

47) The VSEPR theory allows us to determine the
  A) shape of a molecule.
  B) charge on an ion.
  C) color of a compound.
  D) bond type for a molecule.
  E) formula for a compound.

Answer: A

48) When a cation is formed from a representative element
  A) electrons are gained and the ion is larger.
  B) electrons are gained and the ion is smaller.
  C) electrons are lost and the ion is larger.
  D) electrons are lost and the ion is smallerl
  E) the cation acquires a negative charge.

Answer: D

49) The shape of the ammonia molecule (NH_3) is
  A) linear.
  B) square.
  C) pyramidal.
  D) hexagonal.
  E) octagonal.

Answer: C

50) The shape of the water molecule (H_2O) is
  A) linear.
  B) tetrahedral.
  C) pyramidal.
  D) bent
  E) octagonal.

Answer: D

51) The main type of interaction between molecules of ammonia (NH_3) are
  A) ionic bonds.
  B) hydrogen bonds.
  C) polar covalent.
  D) dipole–dipole.
  E) dispersion forces.

Answer: B

52) The main type of interaction between molecules of hydrogen (H_2) are

    A) ionic bonds.
    B) hydrogen bonds.
    C) polar covalent.
    D) dipole–dipole.
    E) dispersion forces.

Answer: E

53) The carbon tetrachloride molecule, CCl_4, has the shape of a

    A) tetrahedron.
    B) square.
    C) cube.
    D) circle.
    E) sphere.

Answer: A

54) The carbon tetrachloride molecule, CCl_4, is

    A) a polar molecule with polar bonds.
    B) a nonpolar molecule with polar bonds.
    C) a nonpolar molecule with nonpolar bonds.
    D) a polar molecule with nonpolar bonds.
    E) a polar molecule with ionic bonds.

Answer: B

55) The ammonia molecule (NH_3) is

    A) a polar molecule with polar bonds.
    B) a nonpolar molecule with polar bonds.
    C) a nonpolar molecule with nonpolar bonds.
    D) a polar molecule with nonpolar bonds.
    E) a polar molecule with ionic bonds.

Answer: A

4.2 Short Answer Questions

Identify each of the following compounds as covalent or ionic.

    1) carbon tetrachloride

    Answer: covalent

    2) potassium oxide

    Answer: ionic

    3) carbon dioxide

    Answer: covalent

    4) dihydrogen sulfide

    Answer: covalent

    5) sodium fluoride

    Answer: ionic

6) nitrogen trichloride

Answer: covalent

4.3 Matching Questions

Match the correct name of the polyatomic ions with the formulas given.

1) NO_3^-

2) CO_3^{2-}

3) SO_4^{2-}

4) SO_3^{2-}

5) PO_4^{3-}

6) NO_2^-

7) HCO_3^-

8) HSO_4^-

9) OH^-

A) phosphate

B) hydroxide

C) oxide

D) hydrogen carbonate

E) sulfite

F) phosphite

G) nitrite

H) nitrate

I) hydrogen sulfate

J) sulfate

K) carbonite

L) carbonate

M) hydrogen sulfite

1) H	2) L	3) J	4) E	5) A	6) G
7) D	8) I	9) B			

Give the correct valence for ions of the following elements.

10) Ca

11) Cl

12) O

13) Al

14) K

A) 2^-

B) 1^-

C) 3^+

D) 1^+

E) 0

F) 2^+

10) F	11) B	12) A	13) C	14) D

Indicate the type of bonding you would expect between the following elements.

15) Na and F

A) none

16) N and F

B) nonpolar covalent

17) F and F

C) polar covalent

18) He and F

D) ionic

19) H and F

15) D   16) C   17) B   18) A   19) C

Match the chemical name with the correct formula.

20) magnesium sulfate

A) $Mg(HSO_3)_2$

21) magnesium hydrogen sulfate

B) $MgSO_3$

22) magnesium sulfide

C) MgS

23) magnesium sulfite

D) $Mg(HSO_4)_2$

24) magnesium hydrogen sulfite

E) $MgSO_4$

20) E   21) D   22) C   23) B   24) A

Chapter 5 Chemical Quantities and Reactions

5.1 Multiple-Choice Questions

1) Which of the following is an example of a physical change?
    A) grinding coffee beans
    B) baking a cake
    C) converting water to hydrogen and oxygen
    D) digesting a cheeseburger
    E) burning coal

Answer: A

2) Which of the following would NOT be a physical change?
    A) freezing water to make ice cubes
    B) tearing a piece of aluminum foil
    C) boiling water for soup
    D) burning gasoline in a lawnmower
    E) melting gold to make jewelry

Answer: D

3) Which of the following is a chemical change?
    A) cutting a rope
    B) bending a steel rod
    C) making a snowman
    D) burning sugar
    E) melting gold

Answer: D

4) Which of the following is a physical change?
    A) baking a cake
    B) dry ice subliming
    C) fermenting grapes to produce wine
    D) digesting a meal
    E) a tomato ripening

Answer: B

5) A chemical equation is balanced when
    A) the total number of molecules is the same in reactants and products.
    B) the total number of ions is the same in reactants and products.
    C) the sum of the coefficients of the reactants is equal to the sum of the coefficients of the products.
    D) the number of atoms of each element is the same in reactants and products.
    E) the charge on each atom is the same in reactants and products.

Answer: D

6) Which of the following gives the balanced equation for this reaction?

$$K_3PO_4 + Ca(NO_3)_2 \rightarrow Ca_3(PO_4)_2 + KNO_3$$

A) $KPO_4 + CaNO_3 + KNO_3$
B) $K_3PO_4 + Ca(NO_3)_2 \rightarrow Ca_3(PO_4)_2 + 3KNO_3$
C) $2 K_3PO_4 + Ca(NO_3)_2 \rightarrow Ca_3(PO_4)_2 + 6KNO_3$
D) $2K_3PO_4 + 3Ca(NO_3)_2 \rightarrow Ca_3(PO_4)_2 + 6KNO_3$
E) $K_3PO_4 + Ca(NO_3)_2 \rightarrow Ca_3(PO_4)_2 + KNO_3$

Answer: D

7) Which of the following correctly gives the best coefficients for the reaction below?

$$N_2H_4 + H_2O_2 \rightarrow N_2 + H_2O$$

A) 1, 1, 1, 1   B) 1, 2, 1, 4   C) 2, 4, 2, 8   D) 1, 4, 1, 4   E) 2, 4, 2, 4

Answer: B

8) What coefficient is placed in front of O_2 to complete the balancing of the following equation?

$$C_5H_8 + ?\ O_2 \rightarrow 5CO_2 + 4H_2O$$

A) 1   B) 3   C) 5   D) 7   E) 9

Answer: D

9) What is the coefficient of hydrogen, H_2, when the following equation is balanced?

$$Al + H_2SO_4 \rightarrow Al_2(SO_4)_3 + ?\ H_2$$

A) 1   B) 2   C) 3   D) 4   E) 5

Answer: C

Pentane (C_5H_{12}) reacts with oxygen (O_2) to form carbon dioxide (CO_2) and water (H_2O) according to the following reaction. Answer the following question(s) about this reaction.

$$C_5H_{12} + ?\ O_2 \rightarrow ?\ CO_2 + ?\ H_2O$$

10) What is the coefficient for oxygen in the balanced equation?
A) 2   B) 4   C) 5   D) 6   E) 8

Answer: E

11) What is the coefficient for carbon dioxide in the balanced equation?
A) 2   B) 4   C) 5   D) 6   E) 8

Answer: C

12) What is the coefficient for water in the balanced equation?
A) 2   B) 4   C) 5   D) 6   E) 8

Answer: D

13) In a _____ reaction, two or more elements or compounds form one product.
   A) decomposition
   B) single replacement
   C) dehydration
   D) double replacement
   E) combination

Answer: E

14) The following reaction takes place when an electric current is passed through water. It is an example of a _____ reaction.

$$2H_2O \xrightarrow{\text{electricity}} 2H_2 + O_2$$

   A) combination
   B) single replacement
   C) dehydration
   D) decomposition
   E) double replacement

Answer: D

15) Which of the following is an oxidation–reduction reaction?
   A) $CaCl_2 + Na_2SO_4 \rightarrow CaSO_4 + 2NaCl$
   B) $KOH + HNO_3 \rightarrow H_2O + KNO_3$
   C) $N_2 + O_2 \rightarrow 2NO$
   D) $AgNO_3 + NaCl \rightarrow AgCl + NaNO_3$
   E) $Al_2(SO_4)_3 + 6KOH \rightarrow 2Al(OH)_3 + 3K_2SO_4$

Answer: C

16) What is oxidized and what is reduced in the following reaction?

$$2Al + 3Br_2 \rightarrow 2AlBr_3$$

   A) Al is oxidized and Br_2 is reduced.
   B) $AlBr_3$ is reduced and Br_2 is oxidized.
   C) Al is reduced and Br_2 is oxidized.
   D) $AlBr_3$ is reduced and Al is oxidized.
   E) $AlBr_3$ is oxidized and Al is reduced.

Answer: A

17) Which of the following describes an oxidation?
   A) loss of electrons or loss of oxygen
   B) loss of electrons or gain of oxygen
   C) loss of electrons or gain of hydrogen
   D) gain of electrons or gain of oxygen
   E) gain of electrons or loss of H

Answer: B

18) In an oxidation–reduction reaction, the substance oxidized always
    A) takes on oxygen atoms.
    B) shows a loss of electrons.
    C) gives up hydrogen atoms.
    D) shows a gain of electrons.
    E) becomes a charged species.

Answer: B

19) In this reaction, what is the substance oxidized?

$$Zn + 2\,HCl \rightarrow ZnCl_2 + H_2$$

    A) chlorine
    B) zinc chloride
    C) hydrogen
    D) Zn
    E) oxygen

Answer: D

20) In an oxidation–reduction reaction, the substance reduced always
    A) takes on oxygen atoms.
    B) shows a loss of electrons.
    C) gives up hydrogen atoms.
    D) shows a gain of electrons.
    E) becomes a charged species.

Answer: D

21) In this reaction, what is the coefficient for calcium oxide?

$$CaO + CO_2 \rightarrow CaCO_3$$

    A) 1   B) 2   C) 3   D) 4   E) 5

Answer: A

22) In this reaction, what is the correct coefficient for sodium chloride?

$$Pb(NO_3)_2 + ?\ NaCl \rightarrow PbCl_2 + ?\ NaNO_3$$

    A) 1   B) 2   C) 3   D) 4   E) 5

Answer: B

23) In the following reaction, what is the correct coefficient for aluminum chloride?

$$Al + Cl_2 \rightarrow AlCl_3$$

    A) 1   B) 2   C) 3   D) 4   E) 5

Answer: B

24) What is the classification for this reaction?

$$SO_3 + H_2O \rightarrow H_2SO_4$$

A) decomposition
B) combination
C) replacement
D) double replacement
E) oxidation reduction

Answer: B

25) The reaction of carbon with oxygen to produce carbon monoxide is an example of which class of reaction?

$$2C + O_2 \rightarrow 2CO$$

A) single replacement
B) double replacement
C) combination
D) catalytic
E) endothermic

Answer: C

26) For the following reaction, what is the correct coefficient for the H_2?

$$Fe + HCl \rightarrow FeCl_3 + H_2$$

A) 1   B) 2   C) 3   D) 4   E) 5

Answer: C

27) What is the classification for this unbalanced reaction?

$$Fe + HCl \rightarrow FeCl_3 + H_2$$

A) dehydration
B) combination
C) decomposition
D) single replacement
E) double replacement

Answer: D

28) In any balanced chemical equation, the number of each type of atom on both sides of the equation is
A) doubled.
B) the same.
C) decreased by one.
D) increased by one.
E) dependent on the temperature.

Answer: B

29) How many moles of water, H_2O, are present in 75.0 g H_2O?
    A) 4.41 moles
    B) 4.17 moles
    C) 75.0 moles
    D) 7.50 moles
    E) 1.35×10^3 moles
Answer: B

30) One mole of particles of any substance contains how many particles?
    A) 10^6
    B) 3×10^{-10}
    C) 3×10^{10}
    D) 6.02×10^{23}
    E) 6.02×10^{-23}
Answer: D

31) Avogadro's number is the number of
    A) particles in 1 mole of a substance.
    B) amu in 1 mole of a substance.
    C) grams in 1 mole of a substance.
    D) moles in 6.02×10^{23} grams of an element.
    E) moles in 6.02×10^{23} amu of an element.
Answer: A

32) The molar mass of potassium is
    A) 19 g.
    B) 31.0 g.
    C) 6.02×10^{23} g.
    D) 39.1 g.
    E) 15g.
Answer: D

33) One mole of helium gas weighs
    A) 1.00 g.   B) 2.00 g.   C) 3.00 g.   D) 4.00 g.   E) 8.00 g.
Answer: D

34) 0.100 mole of lithium weighs
    A) 3.00 g.   B) 0.300 g.   C) 6.94 g.   D) 0.694 g.   E) 0.700 g.
Answer: D

35) Calculate the molar mass of potassium chloride, KCl.
    A) 74.6 g   B) 54.5 g   C) 6.74 g   D) 67.4 g   E) 19.0 g
Answer: A

36) What is the molar mass of copper(II) sulfate, $CuSO_4$?
    A) 16.00 g   B) 63.60.g   C) 111.6 g   D) 159.6 g   E) 319.2 g
Answer: D

37) Calculate the molar mass of magnesium chloride, $MgCl_2$.

    A) 24.3 g   B) 95.3 g   C) 125.9 g   D) 59.8 g   E) 70.0 g

    Answer: B

38) What is the molar mass of sodium phosphate, Na_3PO_4?

    A) 119.2 g   B) 308.0 g   C) 164.0 g   D) 226.1 g   E) 354.0 g

    Answer: C

39) How many moles of carbon atoms are there in 0.500 mole of C_2H_6?

    A) 0.500 mole
    B) 1.00 mole
    C) 3.00 moles
    D) 6.02×10^{23} moles
    E) 4.00 moles

    Answer: B

40) What is the molar mass of sucrose ($C_{12}H_{22}O_{11}$)?

    A) 29.0 g   B) 50.2 g   C) 210.0 g   D) 342.0 g   E) 182.0 g

    Answer: D

41) One mole of neon atoms has a mass of

    A) 6.02×10^{23} g.
    B) 14.0 g.
    C) 10.0 g.
    D) 20.2 g.
    E) 30.2 g.

    Answer: D

42) The molar mass of $C_3H_8O_2$ is

    A) 76.0 g.   B) 60.0 g.   C) 29.0 g.   D) 69.0 g.   E) 52.0 g.

    Answer: A

43) The molar mass of calcium hydroxide, $Ca(OH)_2$, is

    A) 58.1 g.   B) 57.1 g.   C) 74.1 g.   D) 114.2 g.   E) 38.0 g.

    Answer: C

44) What is the molar mass of $Mg_3(PO_4)_2$, a substance formerly used in medicine as an antacid?

    A) 71.3 g   B) 118.3 g   C) 150.3 g   D) 214.3 g   E) 262.9 g

    Answer: E

45) 4.00 moles of sodium have a mass of

    A) 4.60 g.   B) 11.0 g.   C) 23.0 g.   D) 44.0 g.   E) 92.0 g.

    Answer: E

46) How many moles of K_2SO_4 are in 15.0 g of K_2SO_4?

   A) 0.172 moles

   B) 2.61×10^3 moles

   C) 0.111 moles

   D) 0.0861 moles

   E) 0.119 moles

   Answer: D

47) 3.00 moles of NO_2 have a mass of

   A) 138 g.   B) 46.0 g.   C) 30.0 g.   D) 90.0 g.   E) 45.0 g.

   Answer: A

48) How many grams of Fe_2O_3 are there in 0.500 mole of Fe_2O_3?

   A) 79.8 g   B) 35.9 g   C) 63.8 g   D) 51.9 g   E) 160 g

   Answer: A

49) How many grams of glucose ($C_6H_{12}O_6$) are in 3.55 moles of glucose?

   A) 180 g   B) 639 g   C) 103 g   D) 426 g   E) 50.7 g

   Answer: B

50) Given the following equation, what is the correct form of the conversion factor needed to convert the number of moles of O_2 to the number of moles of Fe_2O_3 produced?

$$4Fe \; + \; 3O_2 \rightarrow 2Fe_2O_3$$

   A) $\dfrac{4 \text{ moles Fe}}{3 \text{ moles } O_2}$

   B) $\dfrac{4 \text{ moles Fe}}{2 \text{ moles } Fe_2O_3}$

   C) $\dfrac{3 \text{ moles } O_2}{2 \text{ moles } Fe_2O_3}$

   D) $\dfrac{2 \text{ moles } Fe_2O_3}{4 \text{ moles Fe}}$

   E) $\dfrac{2 \text{ moles } Fe_2O_3}{3 \text{ moles } O_2}$

   Answer: E

For the following question(s), consider the following equation.

$$2Mg + O_2 \rightarrow 2MgO$$

51) The number of moles of oxygen gas needed to react with 4.0 moles of Mg is
    A) 1.0 mole.   B) 2.0 moles.   C) 3.0 moles.   D) 4.0 moles.   E) 6.0 moles.

    Answer: B

52) The number of moles of MgO produced when 0.20 mole of O_2 reacts completely is
    A) 0.10 mole.
    B) 0.20 mole.
    C) 0.40 mole.
    D) 0.60 mole.
    E) 0.80 mole.

    Answer: C

53) How many moles of magnesium are needed to react with 16 g of O_2?
    A) 0.50 mole   B) 1.0 moles   C) 2.0 moles   D) 3.0 moles   E) 4.0 moles

    Answer: B

54) How many grams of MgO are produced when 40.0 grams of O_2 react completely with Mg?
    A) 30.4 g   B) 50.4 g   C) 60.8 g   D) 101 g   E) 201 g

    Answer: D

For the following question(s), consider the following balanced equation.

$$Mg_3N_2 + 6H_2O \rightarrow 3Mg(OH)_2 + 2NH_3$$

55) What is the correct form of the conversion factor needed to convert the number of moles of H_2O to the number of moles of NH_3 produced?

    A) $\dfrac{2 \text{ moles } NH_3}{6 \text{ moles } H_2O}$

    B) $\dfrac{6 \text{ moles } H_2O}{2 \text{ moles } NH_3}$

    C) $\dfrac{1 \text{ mole } Mg_3H_2}{6 \text{ moles } H_2O}$

    D) $\dfrac{18 \text{ g } H_2O}{1 \text{ mole } H_2O}$

    E) $\dfrac{18 \text{ g } H_2O}{17 \text{ g } NH_3}$

    Answer: A

56) When 2 moles of Mg_3N_2 are allowed to react, how many moles of H_2O also react?
   A) 1 mole   B) 4 moles   C) 6 moles   D) 8 moles   E) 12 moles
   Answer: E

57) When 4 moles of aluminum are allowed to react with an excess of chlorine gas, Cl_2, how many moles of aluminum chloride are produced?
   $$2Al + 3Cl_2 \rightarrow 2AlCl_3$$

   A) 1 mole   B) 2 moles   C) 3 moles   D) 4 moles   E) 5 moles
   Answer: D

58) In the reaction of nitrogen gas, N_2, with hydrogen gas, H_2, to form ammonia gas, NH_3, how many moles of hydrogen are needed to react with two moles of nitrogen?
   $$N_2 + 3H_2 \rightarrow 2NH_3$$

   A) 2 moles   B) 4 moles   C) 6 moles   D) 8 moles   E) 10 moles
   Answer: C

59) How many grams of hydrogen are needed to produce 1.80 g of water according to this equation?

   $$2H_2 + O_2 \rightarrow 2H_2O$$

   A) 0.100 g   B) 0.180g   C) 0.200 g   D) 2.00 g   E) 4.00 g
   Answer: C

60) In the reaction of silver nitrate with sodium chloride, how many grams of silver chloride will be produced from 100. g of silver nitrate when it is mixed with an excess of sodium chloride? The equation for the reaction is below.

   $$AgNO_3 + NaCl \rightarrow AgCl + NaNO_3$$

   A) 107.9 g   B) 169.9 g   C) 84.4 g   D) 0.589 g   E) 58.9 g
   Answer: C

For the following question(s), consider the following balanced equation.

   $$Mg_3N_2 + 6H_2O \rightarrow 3Mg(OH)_2 + 2NH_3$$

61) When 2.00 moles of H_2O react, how many grams of NH_3 are produced?
   A) 34.0 g   B) 10.0 g   C) 5.67 g   D) 11.3 g   E) 102 g
   Answer: D

62) How many grams of H_2O are needed to produce 150 g of $Mg(OH)_2$?
   A) 46 g   B) 18 g   C) 130 g   D) 93 g   E) 23 g
   Answer: D

63) Find the mass of $AlCl_3$ that is produced when 25.0 grams of Al_2O_3 react with HCl according to the following equation.

$$Al_2O_3 + 6HCl \rightarrow 2AlCl_3 + 3H_2O$$

A) 155 g   B) 72.9 g   C) 65.4 g   D) 32.6 g   E) 16.3 g

Answer: C

64) How many grams of NO are required to produce 145 g of N_2 in the following reaction?

$$4NH_3 + 6NO \rightarrow 5N_2 + 6H_2O$$

A) 186 g   B) 155 g   C) 125 g   D) 129 g   E) 145 g

Answer: A

65) The _____ is the minimum energy needed for a chemical reaction to begin.
   A) reaction energy
   B) activation energy
   C) energy of reactants
   D) energy of products
   E) heat of reaction

Answer: B

66) How many grams of CO_2 are produced from 125 g of O_2 and excess CH_4 ?
   $$CH_4 + 2O_2 \rightarrow CO_2 + 2H_2O$$
   A) 125 g of CO_2
   B) 62.5 g of CO_2
   C) 172 g of CO_2
   D) 85.9 g of CO_2
   E) 250. g of CO_2

Answer: D

67) A reaction that releases energy as it occurs is classified as a(n) _____.
   A) endothermic reaction
   B) exothermic reaction
   C) oxidation-reduction reaction
   D) catalyzed reaction
   E) decomposition reaction

Answer: B

68) What type of reaction is: $CH_4 + 2O_2 \rightarrow CO_2 + 2H_2O + 218\,kcal$?
   A) an endothermic reaction
   B) an exothermic reaction
   C) a single replacement reaction
   D) a combination reaction
   E) a decomposition reaction

Answer: B

69) How many kcal are produced when 32.0 g of CH_4 react?

$CH_4 + 2O_2 \rightarrow CO_2 + 2H_2O + 218$ kcal

A) 218 kcal   B) 109 kcal   C) 436 kcal   D) 6.81 kcal   E) 698 kcal

Answer: C

70) If the reaction shown below is exothermic, the energy level of the reactants is _____.

$H_2 + O_2 \rightarrow 2H_2O$

A) lower than that of the products
B) higher than that of the products
C) the same as that of the products
D) possibly lower, possibly higher than that of the products
E) higher than the activation energy of the reaction

Answer: B

71) Any reaction that absorbs 150 kcal of energy can be classified as _____.
A) endothermic
B) exothermic
C) activated
D) reduction
E) oxidation

Answer: A

72) The _____ is the energy difference between reactants and products in a chemical reaction.
A) transition energy
B) activation energy
C) product energy
D) overall energy
E) heat of reaction

Answer: E

5.2 Bimodal Questions

1) In this reaction, what is the correct coefficient for hydrogen gas?

$?\,H_2 + ?\,O_2 \rightarrow ?\,H_2O$

A) 1   B) 2   C) 3   D) 4   E) 5

Answer: B

Barium chloride and sodium sulfate react according to the following equation.

$BaCl_2 + Na_2SO_4 \rightarrow BaSO_4 + 2NaCl$

Answer the following question(s) about this reaction.
2) How many moles of barium sulfate are produced from 0.1 mole of barium chloride?
A) 0.01 mole   B) 0.1 mole   C) 0.2 mole   D) 1 mole   E) 2 moles

Answer: B

3) How many grams of barium sulfate can be produced from 0.100 mole of barium chloride?
   A) 1.37 g   B) 2.33 g   C) 23.3 g   D) 137 g   E) 233 g

   Answer: C

4) How many grams of barium chloride are needed to make 100. grams of barium sulfate?
   A) 44.9 g   B) 89.3 g   C) 208.3 g   D) 233.3 g   E) 46.6 g

   Answer: B

Answer the question(s) below about the following reaction.

$$2H_2O_2 \rightarrow 2H_2O + O_2$$

5) How many moles of oxygen gas can 30. g of hydrogen peroxide (H_2O_2) produce, if decomposition is complete?
   A) 0.50 mole   B) 0.88 mole   C) 1.0 mole   D) 2.0 mole   E) 0.44 mole

   Answer: E

6) How many grams of water will 100. grams of hydrogen peroxide produce?
   A) 3600 g   B) 360. g   C) 5.88 g   D) 53.0 g   E) 106 g

   Answer: D

7) How many grams of hydrogen peroxode are needed to produce 25.0 g of oxygen?
   A) 106 g   B) 26.6 g   C) 5.88 g   D) 25.0 g   E) 53.1 g

   Answer: E

8) How many grams of hydrogen peroxide (H_2O_2) are needed to produce 5.0 moles of water?
   A) 90. g   B) 180 g   C) 3060 g   D) 306 g   E) 170 g

   Answer: E

5.3 Short Answer Questions

1) The number of particles in 1 mole of hydrogen gas is _____.

   Answer: 6.02×10^{23}

2) The molar mass of copper(II) nitrate, $Cu(NO_3)_2$ is _____.

   Answer: 188 g

3) What is the mass of 1 mole of argon gas?

   Answer: 40.0 g

4) Acetylene gas, C_2H_2, reacts with oxygen according to the following equation. If 2 moles of acetylene react completely with sufficient oxygen, how many grams of carbon dioxide are produced?

$$2C_2H_2 + 5O_2 \rightarrow 4CO_2 + 2H_2O$$

   Answer: 176 g

5) What type of reaction is the following?

$$2KClO_3 \rightarrow 2KCl + 3O_2$$

Answer: decomposition reaction

6) What type of reaction is the folowing?

$$Zn + 2HCl \rightarrow ZnCl_2 + H_2$$

Answer: single replacement reaction

5.4 True/False Questions

1) The molar mass of silver is 47 g.

Answer: FALSE

2) The molar mass of magnesium is 24.3 g.

Answer: TRUE

3) The mass of one mole of water is 18.0 g.

Answer: TRUE

4) The molar mass of chlorine gas is 35.5 g.

Answer: FALSE

5) The molar mass of copper(II) chloride is 134.6 g.

Answer: TRUE

6) In the reaction of hydrogen gas with oxygen gas to produce water, 1 mole of oxygen gas can produce 2 moles of water, given sufficient hydrogen available.

Answer: TRUE

7) Avogadro's number is the number of grams in a mole.

Answer: FALSE

8) The following is a decomposition reaction.

$$2KClO_3 \rightarrow 2KCl + 3O_2$$

Answer: TRUE

5.5 Matching Questions

Identify each of the following transformations as a chemical or physical change.

1) water evaporating

      A) physical

2) a button falling off of a shirt

      B) chemical

3) silver tarnishing

4) cutting the grass

5) a nail rusting

6) baking a cake

7) placing photographs in a scrapbook

8) formation of green leaves on a plant

9) burning leaves

10) melting ice

1) A	2) A	3) B	4) A	5) B	6) B
7) A	8) B	9) B	10) A		

Chapter 6 Gases

6.1 Multiple-Choice Questions

1) Which of the following is NOT part of the kinetic theory of gases?
   A) A gas is composed of very small particles.
   B) There is very little empty space in a gas.
   C) Gas particles move rapidly.
   D) Gas particles do not attract or repel one another.
   E) Gas particles move faster when the temperature increases.

   Answer: B

2) According to the kinetic theory of gases, a gas can be compressed much more than a liquid or solid because
   A) a gas is composed of very small particles.
   B) the particles of a gas are very far apart.
   C) gas particles move rapidly.
   D) gas particles do not attract or repel one another.
   E) gas particles move faster when the temperature increases.

   Answer: B

3) According to the kinetic theory of gases, particles of a gas
   A) are very large particles.
   B) are very far apart.
   C) lose their valence electrons.
   D) move slowly.
   E) decrease kinetic energy as temperature increases.

   Answer: B

4) In the kinetic molecular theory of gas behavior, particles of a gas tend to move _____ and collisions between them are _____.
   A) rapidly, rare
   B) slowly, rare
   C) rapidly, elastic
   D) slowly, elastic
   E) slowly, unusual

   Answer: C

5) The force of gas particles against the walls of a container is called
   A) pressure.
   B) volume.
   C) temperature.
   D) quantity of gas.
   E) density.

   Answer: A

6) Which measurement describes the pressure of a gas?
   A) 315 K
   B) 1.2 g/L
   C) 2.5 L
   D) 725 mm Hg
   E) 0.45 moles

Answer: D

7) The unit of 1 atmosphere used to describe the pressure of a gas is equal to
   A) 1 mm Hg.
   B) 100 mm Hg.
   C) 200 mm Hg.
   D) 600 mm Hg.
   E) 760 mm Hg.

Answer: E

8) A 5.00-L tank contains helium gas at 1.50 atm. What is the pressure of the gas in mm Hg?
   A) 1.50 mm Hg
   B) 507 mm Hg
   C) 760 mm Hg
   D) 1140 mm Hg
   E) 3800 mm Hg

Answer: D

9) In response to Boyle's law, the pressure of a gas increases as the volume decreases because
   A) the gas particles get bigger.
   B) the kinetic energy of the gas particles increases.
   C) the temperature of the gas increases.
   D) the gas particles strike the walls of the container with more force.
   E) the gas particles strike the walls of the container more often.

Answer: E

10) Which of the following correctly describes the process of inspiration (air entering the lungs)?
    A) The lungs expand, causing their internal pressure to decrease.
    B) The lungs expand, causing their internal pressure to increase.
    C) The lungs contract, causing their internal pressure to decrease.
    D) The lungs contract, causing their internal pressure to increase.
    E) There is no change in the internal pressure in the lungs.

Answer: A

11) The volume of a gas with a pressure of 1.2 atm increases from 1.0 L to 4.0 L. What is the final pressure of the gas, assuming constant temperature?
    A) 1.2 atm   B) 0.30 atm   C) 3.3 atm   D) 4.8 atm   E) 1.0 atm

Answer: B

12) The pressure of 5.0 L of gas increases from 1.50 atm to 1240 mm Hg. What is the final volume of the gas, assuming constant temperature?
    A) 4100 L   B) 5.0 L   C) 0.0060 L   D) 5.4 L   E) 4.6 L

Answer: E

A balloon is filled with helium gas. For the following question(s), select the letter of the balloon diagram that corresponds to the given change in conditions.

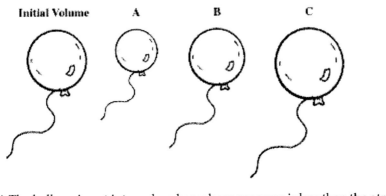

Initial Volume   A   B   C

13) The balloon is put into a chamber whose pressure is less than the atmospheric pressure.
   A) A   B) B   C) C   D) A and B   E) B and C

Answer: C

14) The temperature is changed from 50 °C to –150 °C at constant pressure.
   A) A   B) B   C) C   D) A and B   E) B and C

Answer: A

15) Complete the following statement: In Charles' law, the volume of a gas _____ when the _____ decreases.
   A) increases, temperature
   B) increases, quantity of gas
   C) increases, pressure
   D) decreases, temperature
   E) decreases, pressure

Answer: D

16) What unit of temperature is used in gas law calculations?
   A) Fahrenheit
   B) Celsius
   C) Kelvin
   D) either Celsius or Fahrenheit
   E) either Celsius or Kelvin

Answer: C

17) A temperature of 125 °C is the same as _____ K.
   A) –148 K   B) 398 K   C) 257 K   D) 530. K   E) 273 K

Answer: B

18) The gas with an initial volume of 24.0 L at a pressure of 565 mmHg is compressed until the volume is 16.0 L. What is the final pressure of the gas, assuming the temperature does not change?
   A) 377 mmHg
   B) 760 mmHg
   C) 848 mmHg
   D) 500. mmHg
   E) 465 mmHg

Answer: C

19) The temperature of a 500. mL sample of gas increases from 150. K to 350. K. What is the final volume of the sample of gas, if the pressure in the container is kept constant?
   A) 210 mL
   B) 1170 mL
   C) 0.0095 mL
   D) 0.0047 mL
   E) 110 mL

Answer: B

20) In Gay-Lussac's law, the pressure of a gas increases due to an increase in temperature because
   A) the molecules strike the walls of the container less often.
   B) the molecules strike the walls of the container more often.
   C) the molecules get bigger.
   D) there is a decrease in the volume of the container.
   E) there is an increase in the number of gas particles.

Answer: B

21) A gas contained in a steel tank has a pressure of 1.5 atm at a temperature of 320 K. What will be the gas pressure when the temperature changes to 450 K?
   A) 1.5 atm   B) 0.94 atm   C) 0.47 atm   D) 2.1 atm   E) 1.1 atm

Answer: D

22) At 570. mm Hg and 25 °C, a gas sample has a volume of 2270 mL. What is the final pressure (in mm Hg) at a volume of 1250 mL and a temperature of 175 °C?
   A) 1560 mm Hg
   B) 210 mm Hg
   C) 7000 mm Hg
   D) 690 mm Hg
   E) 470 mm Hg

Answer: A

23) According to Avogrado's law,
   A) the volume of a gas is inversely related to the number of moles at constant temperature and pressure.
   B) the volume of a gas is inversely related to the number of moles at standard temperature and pressure.
   C) the volume of a gas depends only on the temperature and pressure.
   D) the volume of a gas depends only on the number of moles in the sample.
   E) the volume of a gas is directly related to the number of moles at constant temperature and pressure.

Answer: E

24) At STP, temperature and pressure have the values of
   A) 0 K and 1 atm.
   B) 273 K and 1 mm Hg.
   C) 273 K and 760 mm Hg.
   D) 0 K and 760 mm Hg.
   E) 760 K and 273 atm.

   Answer: C

25) A gas sample contains 4.0 g of CH_4 and 2.0 g of He. What is the volume of the sample at STP?
   A) 130 L   B) 11 L   C) 17 L   D) 30. L   E) 5.6 L

   Answer: C

26) A gas sample containing 12.0 g of CH_4 has a volume of 14.0 L. What will the volume be if 12.0
   g of He is added? (Temperature and pressure do not change.)
   A) 28.0 L   B) 52.5 L   C) 56.0 L   D) 70.0 L   E) 3.50 L

   Answer: D

27) A diver exhales a bubble with a volume of 250 mL at a pressure of 2.4 atm and a temperature of
   15 °C. What is the volume of the bubble when it reaches the surface where the pressure is 1.0
   atm and the temperature is 27 °C?
   A) 580 mL   B) 630 mL   C) 100 mL   D) 110 mL   E) 1100 mL

   Answer: B

28) How many moles of neon occupy a volume of 14.3 L at STP?
   A) 36.7 moles
   B) 32.0 moles
   C) 6.45 moles
   D) 0.638 moles
   E) 1.57 moles

   Answer: D

29) 1 mole of a gas occupies 22.4 L at
   A) 0 °C and 0.50 atm.
   B) 0 °C and 760 mm Hg.
   C) 100 °C and 1 atm.
   D) 100 °C and 10 atm.
   E) 0 K and 1 atm.

   Answer: B

30) At STP conditions, 11 g of SO_2 have a volume of
   A) 250 L.   B) 3.8 L.   C) 22 L.   D) 0.0076 L.   E) 130 L.

   Answer: B

31) The total pressure in a mixture of gases is equal to the partial pressure(s) of
   A) the gas with the greatest number of moles.
   B) the gas with the smallest number of moles.
   C) the gas with the highest molecular weight.
   D) the gas that occupies the largest volume.
   E) all the gases added together.

   Answer: E

32) A cyclopropane–oxygen mixture is used as an anesthetic. If the partial pressure of cyclopropane in the mixture is 330 mm Hg and the partial pressure of the oxygen is 1.0 atm, what is the total pressure of the mixture in torr?
    A) 330 torr   B) 430 torr   C) 760 torr   D) 1.4 torr   E) 1100 torr

Answer: E

33) A tank contains helium gas at 490 mm Hg, nitrogen gas at 0.75 atm, and neon at 520 torr. What is the total pressure in atm?
    A) 2.1 atm
    B) 0.55 atm
    C) 1.0×10^3 atm
    D) 1.5 atm
    E) 1600 atm

Answer: A

34) Which of the following correctly describes the partial pressures of gases in the body?
    A) high O_2, low CO_2, oxygenated blood
    B) high O_2, low CO_2, deoxygenated blood
    C) high O_2, high CO_2, oxygenated blood
    D) high O_2, high CO_2, tissue
    E) low O_2, low CO_2, deoxygenated blood

Answer: A

35) Which of the following is NOT a potential use for a hyperbaric chamber?
    A) treatment for burns and infections
    B) counteracting carbon monoxide poisoning
    C) increasing the rate at which a broken bone heals
    D) treating a diver with the bends
    E) treating some cancers

Answer: C

36) In the kinetic molecular theory of gas behavior, the assumption is made that gas molecules
    A) move rapidly in random directions.
    B) are attracted to each other by strong forces.
    C) are close together in their container.
    D) move with a kinetic energy equal to their centigrade temperature.
    E) occasionally come to rest.

Answer: A

37) The pressure exerted by a gas on its container is directly proportional to
    A) the volume of the container.
    B) the mass of the individual gas molecules.
    C) the centigrade temperature of the gas.
    D) the number of molecules of gas in the sample.
    E) the Fahrenheit temperature of the gas.

Answer: D

38) At constant temperature, a sample of helium at 760. torr in a closed container was compressed from 5.00 L to 3.00 L. What was the new pressure exerted by the helium on its container?
   A) 800. torr   B) 2280 torr   C) 15.0 torr   D) 3800 torr   E) 1270 torr
   Answer: E

39) A gas sample in a closed, expandable container of initial volume 5.00 L was allowed to warm from 25 °C to 35 °C. What was its new volume?
   A) 4.84 L   B) 5.17 L   C) 7.00 L   D) 3.57 L   E) 4380 L
   Answer: B

40) A gas at 5.00 atm pressure was stored in a tank during the winter at 5.0 °C. During the summer, the temperature in the storage area reached 40.0 °C. What was the pressure in the gas tank then?
   A) 0.625 atm   B) 4.44 atm   C) 5.63 atm   D) 40.0 atm   E) 69.5 atm
   Answer: C

41) A sample of nitrogen gas had a volume of 500. mL, a pressure in its closed container of 740 torr, and a temperature of 25 °C. What was the new volume of the gas when the temperature was changed to 50 °C and the new pressure was 760 torr?
   A) 530 mL   B) 450 mL   C) 970 mL   D) 240 mL   E) 400 mL
   Answer: A

42) At STP, what is the volume of 4.50 moles of nitrogen gas?
   A) 167 L   B) 3420 L   C) 101 L   D) 60.7 L   E) 1230 L
   Answer: C

43) At STP, how many moles of helium would occupy 1.00 L?
   A) 2.24 moles
   B) 224 moles
   C) 22.4 moles
   D) 0.446 moles
   E) 0.0446 moles
   Answer: E

44) A sample of argon at 300. °C and 50.0 atm pressure is cooled in the same container to a temperature of 0. °C. What is the new pressure?
   A) 105 atm   B) 45.5 atm   C) 54.9 atm   D) 23.8 atm   E) 42.7 atm
   Answer: D

45) At STP, what is the volume of 1.0 mole of carbon dioxide?
   A) 1.00 L   B) 44.0 L   C) 273 L   D) 22.4 L   E) 12.2 L
   Answer: D

46) At STP, what is the mass 13.0 L of methane, CH_4?
   A) 0.580 g   B) 16.0 g   C) 9.29 g   D) 27.6 g   E) 22.4 g
   Answer: C

47) $Zn(s) + 2 HCl(aq) \rightarrow H_2(g) + ZnCl_2(aq)$
   When 25.0 g of Zn reacts, how many L of H_2 gas are formed at STP?
   A) 4.28 L   B) 0.0171 L   C) 8.56 L   D) 22.4 L   E) 0.382 L
   Answer: C

48) $Zn(s) + 2 HCl(aq) \rightarrow H_2(g) + ZnCl_2(aq)$

If 1.26 L of H_2 gas are formed at STP, how many g of HCl reacted?

A) 0.0563 g   B) 0.113 g   C) 2.05 g   D) 4.11 g   E) 36.5 g

Answer: D

49) $4 Na(s) + O_2(g) \rightarrow 2Na_2O(s)$

How many L of O_2 gas at STP, are needed to react with 15.0 g of Na?

A) 3.65 L   B) 14.6 L   C) 7.30 L   D) 22.4 L   E) 32.0 L

Answer: A

50) $2KClO_3(s) \rightarrow 2KCl(s) + 3O_2(g)$

How many L of O_2 gas at STP are formed when 15.0 g of $KClO_3$ reacts?

A) 1.83 L   B) 2.74 L   C) 7.30 L   D) 22.4 L   E) 4.11 L

Answer: E

6.2 Short Answer Questions

1) Nitrogen makes up about _____ percent of the atmosphere.
Answer: 78%

2) A barometer is usually filled with _____.
Answer: mercury

3) One atmosphere is the same as _____ mm Hg.
Answer: 760 mm Hg

4) A temperature of 273 °C is the same as _____ K.
Answer: 546 K

5) STP is _____ mm Hg and _____.
Answer: 760 mm Hg; 273 K

6) The pressure unit 1 mm Hg is the same pressure unit as the pressure unit _____.
Answer: 1 torr

6.3 True/False Questions

1) STP stands for 0 °C and 760 mm Hg.
Answer: TRUE

2) The volume of 1 mole of any gas at STP is 22.4 L.
Answer: TRUE

3) The air we breathe is about 21% oxygen.
Answer: TRUE

4) During inspiration, we use 100% of the oxygen in the air we breathe.
Answer: FALSE

5) In deoxygenated blood, the partial pressure of carbon dioxide is greater than the partial pressure of oxygen left.

Answer: TRUE

6) Gas law calculations normally require the use of the Kelvin temperature scale.

Answer: TRUE

7) At 0 K, all motion stops.

Answer: TRUE

8) The pressure exerted by a gas on its container is inversely related to its Kelvin temperature.

Answer: FALSE

9) The pressure increases as the volume increases , if temperature does not change.

Answer: FALSE

10) The speed of gas molecules is related to the volume of the container.

Answer: FALSE

11) The kinetic energy of a gas sample is directly proportional to the Kelvin temperature of the gas.

Answer: TRUE

6.4 Matching Questions

Indicate the effect of each change upon the pressure of a gas.

1) decrease in volume (n, T constant)

2) removing some molecules of gas

3) The temperature is doubled.

4) The volume and the Kelvin temperature are reduced by one-half.

5) A leak occurs and gas escapes.

6) One mole of gas is added.

A) no change

B) increases

C) decreases

1) B   2) C   3) B   4) A   5) C   6) B

Chapter 7 Solutions

7.1 Multiple-Choice Questions

1) The O–H bond in water is polar because
   A) it is an ionic bond.
   B) oxygen is much more electronegative than hydrogen.
   C) oxygen occupies more space than hydrogen.
   D) hydrogen is much more electronegative than oxygen.
   E) it is a hydrogen bond.

   Answer: B

2) A hydrogen bond is
   A) an attraction between a hydrogen atom attached to N, O, or F and an N, O, or F atom.
   B) a covalent bond between H and O.
   C) an ionic bond between H and another atom.
   D) a bond that is stronger than a covalent bond.
   E) the polar O–H bond in water.

   Answer: A

3) In a solution, the solvent
   A) is a liquid.
   B) can be a liquid or gas.
   C) can be a solid, liquid, or gas.
   D) is never a solid.
   E) is the substance present in the smallest concentration.

   Answer: C

4) Which of the following molecules can form hydrogen bonds?
   A) CH_4 B) NaH   C) NH_3 D) BH_3 E) HI

   Answer: C

5) A solution is prepared by dissolving 2 g of KCl in 100 g of H_2O. In this solution, H_2O is the
   A) solute.
   B) solvent.
   C) solution.
   D) solid.
   E) ionic compound.

   Answer: B

6) Oil does not dissolve in water because
   A) oil is polar.
   B) oil is nonpolar.
   C) water is nonpolar.
   D) water is saturated.
   E) oil is hydrated.

   Answer: B

7) When KCl dissolves in water
    A) the Cl^- ions are attracted to dissolved K^+ ions.
    B) the Cl^- ions are attracted to the partially negative oxygen atoms of the water molecule.
    C) the K^+ ions are attracted to Cl^- ions on the KCl crystal.
    D) the K^+ ions are attracted to the partially negative oxygen atoms of the water molecule.
    E) the K^+ ions are attracted to the partially positive hydrogen atoms of the water molecule.
    Answer: D

8) Water is a polar solvent and hexane (C_6H_{14}) is a nonpolar solvent. Which of the following correctly describes the solubility of the solute?
    A) mineral oil, soluble in water
    B) $CaCl_2$, soluble in hexane
    C) $NaHCO_3$, soluble in water
    D) CCl_4, soluble in water
    E) octane, soluble in water
    Answer: C

9) In water, a substance that ionizes completely in solution is called a
    A) weak electrolyte.
    B) nonelectrolyte.
    C) semiconductor.
    D) nonconductor.
    E) strong electrolyte.
    Answer: E

10) An equivalent is
    A) the amount of ion that has a 1+ charge.
    B) the amount of ion that has a 1- charge.
    C) the amount of ion that carries 1 mole of electrical charge.
    D) 1 mole of any ion.
    E) 1 mole of an ionic compound.
    Answer: C

11) When some of the sugar added to iced tea remains undissolved at the bottom of the glass, the solution is
    A) dilute.
    B) polar.
    C) nonpolar.
    D) saturated.
    E) unsaturated.
    Answer: D

12) The solubility of KI is 50 g in 100 g of H_2O at 20 °C. If 110 grams of KI are added to 200 grams of H_2O,
    A) all of the KI will dissolve.
    B) the solution will freeze.
    C) the solution will start boiling.
    D) a saturated solution will form.
    E) the solution will be unsaturated.

Answer: D

13) An increase in the temperature of a solution usually
    A) increases the boiling point.
    B) increases the solubility of a gas in the solution.
    C) increases the solubility of a solid solute in the solution.
    D) decreases the solubility of a solid solute in the solution.
    E) decreases the solubility of a liquid solute in the solution.

Answer: C

14) The mass/mass percent concentration refers to
    A) grams of solute in 1 kg of solvent.
    B) grams of solute in 1 kg of solution.
    C) grams of solute in 100 g of solvent.
    D) grams of solute in 100 g of solution.
    E) grams of solvent in 100 g of solution.

Answer: D

15) What is the concentration, in $m/m\%$, of a solution prepared from 50.0 g NaCl and 150.0 g of water?
    A) 0.250%   B) 33.3%   C) 40.0%   D) 25.0%   E) 3.00%

Answer: D

16) Rubbing alcohol is 70.% isopropyl alcohol by volume. How many mL of isopropyl alcohol are in a 1 pint (473 mL) container?
    A) 70. mL   B) 0.15 mL   C) 680 mL   D) 470 mL   E) 330 mL

Answer: E

17) What is the concentration, in $m/v\%$, of a solution prepared from 50. g NaCl and 2.5 L of water?
    A) 5.0%   B) 2.0%   C) 0.020%   D) 0.050%   E) 20.%

Answer: B

18) How many grams of glucose are needed to prepare 400. mL of a 2.0%(m/v) glucose solution?
    A) 800. g   B) 0.0050 g   C) 8.0 g   D) 2.0 g   E) 200. g

Answer: C

19) What volume (mL) of a 15% (m/v) NaOH solution contains 120 g NaOH?
    A) 18 mL
    B) 0.13 mL
    C) 13 mL
    D) 120 mL
    E) 8.0×10^2 mL

Answer: E

20) How many milliliters of a 25% (*m/v*) NaOH solution would contain 75 g of NaOH?
    A) 25 mL
    B) 75 mL
    C) 33 mL
    D) 19 mL
    E) 3.0×10^2 mL

Answer: E

21) A homogeneous mixture that does not settle out upon standing is
    A) an element.
    B) a colloid.
    C) a suspension.
    D) solid.
    E) hydrated.

Answer: B

22) In the process known as osmosis, _____ moves through a semipermeable membrane into an area of _____ concentration.
    A) solute, lower solute
    B) solute, higher solute
    C) solvent, lower solute
    D) solvent, lower solvent
    E) solvent, higher solvent

Answer: D

For the following question(s), consider a 4% starch solution and a 10% starch solution separated by a semipermeable membrane.

23) Which starch solution will decrease in volume as osmosis occurs?
    A) 4%
    B) 10%
    C) Neither exerts osmotic pressure.
    D) They exert equal osmotic pressures.
    E) They exert opposite osmotic pressures.

Answer: A

24) The process that occurs in this system is
    A) filtration.
    B) hydration.
    C) neutralization.
    D) dialysis.
    E) osmosis.

Answer: E

25) Which of the following also occurs in this system?
    A) Water flows equally in both directions.
    B) There is a net flow of water from the 4% starch solution into the 10% starch solution.
    C) There is a net flow of water from the 10% starch solution into the 4% starch solution.
    D) Water does not cross the membrane at all.
    E) Starch moves out of the 10% starch solution into the 4% starch solution.

Answer: B

26) A solution with the same osmotic pressure as the blood is
    A) isotonic to the blood.
    B) hypotonic to the blood.
    C) hypertonic to the blood.
    D) nontonic to the blood.
    E) molar to the blood.

Answer: A

27) A 10% starch solution is separated from a 2% starch solution by a semipermeable membrane. Starch is a colloid. Which of the folloowing is correct?
    A) The 10% solution has the higher osmotic pressure.
    B) The 2% solution has the higher osmotic pressure.
    C) Neither solution has osmotic pressure.
    D) The solutions have the same osmotic pressure.
    E) The solutions have opposite osmotic pressures.

Answer: A

28) A solution that has an osmotic pressure less than that of red blood cells is called
    A) saturated.
    B) hypertonic.
    C) isotonic.
    D) hypotonic.
    E) unsaturated.

Answer: D

29) A red blood cell will undergo crenation in
    A) water.
    B) 0.5% NaCl.
    C) 3% glucose.
    D) 5% glucose.
    E) 7% NaCl.

Answer: E

30) Which solution is isotonic to a red blood cell?
    A) water
    B) 0.5% NaCl
    C) 2% glucose
    D) 0.9% NaCl
    E) 10% glucose

Answer: D

31) A red blood cell will undergo hemolysis in
    A) water.
    B) 0.9% NaCl.
    C) 5% glucose.
    D) 5% NaCl.
    E) 10% glucose.

Answer: A

32) The process by which a semipermeable membrane allows water molecules, small molecules, and ions to pass through while retaining large particles is called
    A) osmotic pressure.
    B) dialysis.
    C) solvation.
    D) dilution.
    E) hydration.

Answer: B

33) An aqueous mixture containing starch (a colloid), NaCl, glucose, and albumin (a colloid) is placed in a dialyzing bag and immersed in distilled water. Which of the following correctly describes the location of the indicated substance after dialysis?
    A) albumin inside
    B) starch outside
    C) albumin inside and outside
    D) water inside only
    E) starch inside and outside

Answer: A

34) What is the molarity of a solution that contains 17 g of NH_3 in 0.50 L of solution?
    A) 34 M   B) 2.0 M   C) 0.50 M   D) 0.029 M   E) 1.0 M

Answer: B

35) The molarity (M) of a solution refers to
    A) moles of solute/L of solution.
    B) moles of solute/ L of solvent.
    C) moles of solute/100 mL of solution.
    D) grams of solute/100 mL of solution.
    E) grams of solute/L of solution.

Answer: A

36) What is the molarity of a solution containing 5.0 moles of KCl in 2.0 L of solution?
    A) 2.5 M   B) 1.0 M   C) 5.0 M   D) 10. M   E) 2.0 M

Answer: A

37) What is the molarity of a solution which contains 58.5 g of sodium chloride dissolved in 0.500 L of solution?
    A) 0.500 M   B) 1.00 M   C) 1.50 M   D) 2.00 M   E) 4.00 M

Answer: D

38) How many moles of $CaCl_2$ are in 250 mL of a 3.0 M of $CaCl_2$ solution?
    A) 750 moles
    B) 1.3 moles
    C) 83 moles
    D) 0.75 mole
    E) 3.0 moles

Answer: D

39) What volume of a 1.5 M KOH solution is needed to provide 3.0 moles of KOH?
    A) 3.0 L   B) 0.50 L   C) 2.0 L   D) 4.5 L   E) 0.22 L

Answer: C

40) During the process of diluting a solution to a lower concentration,
    A) the amount of solute does not change.
    B) the amount of solvent does not change.
    C) there is more solute in the concentrated solution.
    D) the volume of the solution does not change.
    E) water is removed from the concentrated solution.

Answer: A

41) According to Henry's law, the solubility of a gas in a liquid
    A) decreases as the gas pressure above the liquid increases.
    B) increases as the gas pressure above the liquid increases.
    C) remains the same as the temperature increases.
    D) depends on the liquid polarity.
    E) depends on the liquid density.

Answer: B

42) What is the molarity of a KCl solution made by diluting 75.0 mL of a 0.200 M solution to a final volume of 100. mL?
    A) 0.267 M   B) 0.150 M   C) 0.200 M   D) 6.67 M   E) 0.100 M

Answer: B

43) What volume of 2.5% (m/v) KOH can be prepared from 125 mL of a 5.0% KOH solution?
    A) 0.0040 mL
    B) 63 mL
    C) 0.10 mL
    D) 125 mL
    E) 250 mL

Answer: E

44) What volume of 0.10 M NaOH can be prepared from 250. mL of 0.30 M NaOH?
    A) 0.075 L   B) 0.25 L   C) 0.75 L   D) 0.083 L   E) 750 L

Answer: C

45) What volume of a 2.00 M KCl solution is required to prepare 500. mL of a 0.100 M KCl solution?
    A) 0.0400 mL
    B) 25.0 mL
    C) 2.00 mL
    D) 1.00×10^4 mL
    E) 5.00×10^2 mL

Answer: B

46) What is the new mass/volume (m/v)% of a KOH solution that is prepared by diluting 110 mL of a 6% (m/v) KOH solution to 330 mL?
    A) 2%   B) 1%   C) 6%   D) 12%   E) 18%

Answer: A

47) What volume of a 0.12 M KOH solution is needed to react with 23. mL of 0.22 M HCl?
    The reaction is: KOH + HCl → KCl + H_2O
    A) 23 mL   B) 12 mL   C) 42 m L   D) 4.6 mL   E) 16 mL

Answer: C

48) What mass of KCl is in 350 mL of 0.24 M KCl?
   A) 0.84 g   B) 1.1.g   C) 84 g   D) 18 g   E) 6.3 g

   Answer: E

49) How many L of H_2 gas (at STP) is produced from 470 mL of 0.36 M HCl and excess Zn?
   The reaction is: $Zn + 2 HCl \rightarrow Zn Cl_2 + H_2$
   A) 0.17 L   B) 0.85 L   C) 1.9 L   D) 3.8 L   E) 22.4 L

   Answer: C

50) If 28 mL of NaCl reacts completely with 46. mL of 0.44.M $AgNO_3$, what is the molarity of the NaCl solution?
   The reaction is: $AgNO_3 + NaCl \rightarrow AgCl + NaNO_3$
   A) 0.44 M   B) 0.27 M   C) 0.18 M   D) 0.12 M   E) 0.72 M

   Answer: E

7.2 Bimodal Questions

1) Acetic acid can be classified as a _____.
   A) gas
   B) solid
   C) weak electrolyte
   D) strong electrolyte
   E) ionic compound

   Answer: C

2) Using a kidney machine to remove waste products from the blood is known as _____.
   A) osmosis
   B) osmolysis
   C) autolysis
   D) hemolysis
   E) hemodialysis

   Answer: E

3) A _____ will pass through a filter but not a semipermeable memebrane.
   A) solid
   B) precipitate
   C) solution
   D) suspension
   E) colloid

   Answer: E

4) The molarity of a solution of 5.0 g of KCl in 100. mL of solution is _____.
   A) 0.038 M   B) 0.067 M   C) 0.67 M   D) 0.13 M   E) 1.3 M

   Answer: C

7.3 Short Answer Questions

1) The number of moles of a compound dissolved in one liter of a solution is called the

   _____.

   Answer: molarity

2) A substance that carries an electric current when dissolved in water is called a(n) _____.

Answer: electrolyte

3) A substance that produces only a small number of ions in solution is known as a _____ electrolyte.

Answer: weak

4) Substances whose particles pass through filters but cannot pass through semipermeable membranes are called _____.

Answer: colloids

5) A 2.0% (m/v) NaCl solution contains _____ g NaCl in 300. mL of solution.

Answer: 6.0 g

6) A solution which has 12 g of solute dissolved in 200.mL of solution has a m/v concentration of _____.

Answer: 6.0%

7.4 Matching Questions

Identify the term defined in each description.

1) a solution that contains the highest amount of solute that dissolves at a given temperature

A) saturated

B) hypotonic

C) hypertonic

2) the major attraction between water molecules

D) unsaturated

3) the association of several water molecules with ions produced in a solution

E) hydrogen bonding

F) hydration

4) a solution in which more solute can be dissolved

5) a solution that has a higher osmotic pressure than the red blood cells of the body

1) A   2) E   3) F   4) D   5) C

Match the type of mixture with the appropriate characteristics.

6) a mixture of sodium chloride in water

    A) solution

7) a mixture whose particles settle on standing

    B) suspension

    C) colloid

8) a homogeneous mixture in which suspended particles cannot pass through a semipermeable membrane

9) a mixture whose particles cannot be separated by filters or semipermeable membranes

10) a mixture whose particles can be separated by filters

6) A   7) B   8) C   9) A   10) B

Compare the osmotic pressure of these solutions to the osmotic pressure of red blood cells.

11) water

    A) hypertonic

12) 0.5% NaCl

    B) hypotonic

13) 0.9% glucose

    C) isotonic

14) 7% glucose

15) 5% NaCl

16) 5% glucose

17) 0.9% NaCl

11) B   12) B   13) B   14) A   15) A   16) C
17) C

Indicate whether each of the following compounds dissolves in water to give ions, molecules, or both.

18) NaCl, a strong electrolyte   A) both

19) urea, a nonelectrolyte   B) ions

20) HF, a weak electrolyte   C) molecules

21) CH_3CH_2OH, a nonelectrolyte

22) KNO_3, a soluble salt

23) glucose, a nonelectrolyte

24) H_2CO_3, a weak electrolyte

18) B   19) C   20) A   21) C   22) B   23) C
24) A

Chapter 8 Acids and Bases

8.1 Multiple-Choice Questions

1) According to the Arrhenius concept, if HNO_3 were dissolved in water, it would act as
    A) a base.
    B) an acid.
    C) a source of hydroxide ions.
    D) a source of H^- ions.
    E) a proton acceptor.
    Answer: B

2) The name given to an aqueous solution of HBr is
    A) hydrogen bromide.
    B) hydrobromic acid.
    C) bromic acid.
    D) bromous acid.
    E) hypobromous acid.
    Answer: B

3) Which one of the following is characteristic of a base?
    A) produces H_3O^+ in water
    B) has a sour taste
    C) has a slippery, soapy feel
    D) turns blue litmus red
    E) is insoluble in water
    Answer: C

4) Which one of the following is characteristic of an acid?
    A) produces H_3O^+ in water
    B) has a bitter taste
    C) has a slippery, soapy feel
    D) turns litmus blue
    E) is insoluble in water
    Answer: A

5) According to the Bronsted-Lowry definition,
    A) an acid is a proton acceptor.
    B) a base produces H^+ ions in aqueous solutions.
    C) a base is a proton donor.
    D) a base is a proton acceptor.
    E) an acid acts as the solvent.
    Answer: D

6) Identify the Bronsted–Lowry acid in the following reaction.

$$H_2O + CO_3^{2-} \rightarrow HCO_3^- + OH^-$$

A) H_2O B) CO_3^{2-} C) HCO_3^- D) OH^- E) H_2CO_3

Answer: A

7) The correct formula for sulfuric acid is

A) H_2SO_4.   B) H_2SO_3.   C) $H_2SO_4^-$.   D) $H_2SO_3^-$.   E) SO_4^{2-}.

Answer: A

8) The name of $Al(OH)_3$ is
    A) aluminum trihydroxide.
    B) monoaluminum trihydroxide.
    C) aluminum hydroxide.
    D) aluminum(III) hydroxide.
    E) aluminum oxygen hydride.

Answer: C

9) The conjugate acid of H_2O is _____.

    A) H_3O^+

    B) OH^-
    C) H_2O

    D) H^+
    E) H_2O has no conjugate acid.

Answer: A

10) The conjugate base of H_2O is _____.

    A) H_3O^+

    B) OH^-
    C) H_2O

    D) O^{2-}
    E) H_2O has no conjugate base.

Answer: B

11) Which of the following statements correctly describes the hydronium–hydroxide balance in the given solution?
    A) In acids, $[OH^-]$ is greater than $[H_3O^+]$.

    B) In bases, $[OH^-] = [H_3O^+]$.

    C) In neutral solutions, $[H_3O^+] = [H_2O]$.

    D) In bases, $[OH^-]$ is greater than $[H_3O^+]$.

    E) In bases, $[OH^-]$ is less than $[H_3O^+]$.

Answer: D

12) For K_W, the product of $[H_3O^+]$ and $[OH^-]$ is
    A) 1.0×10^{-14}.
    B) 1.0×10^{-7}.
    C) 1.0×10^{-1}.
    D) 1.0.
    E) 1.0×10^{14}.
    Answer: A

13) What is the $[H_3O^+]$ in a solution with $[OH^-] = 1 \times 10^{-12}$ M?
    A) 1×10^{-12} M
    B) 1×10^2 M
    C) 1×10^{-7} M
    D) 1×10^{-8} M
    E) 1×10^{-2} M
    Answer: E

14) What is the $[OH^-]$ in a solution that has a $[H_3O^+] = 1 \times 10^{-6}$ M?
    A) 1×10^{-2} M
    B) 1×10^{-6} M
    C) 1×10^{-8} M
    D) 1×10^{-10} M
    E) 1×10^{-12} M
    Answer: C

15) A solution with a pH of 4 is
    A) extremely acidic.
    B) moderately acidic.
    C) neutral.
    D) slightly basic.
    E) extremely basic.
    Answer: B

16) What is the pH of a solution with $[H_3O^+] = 1 \times 10^{-9}$ M?
    A) 1.0×10^{-5} B) -9.0 C) 5.0 D) -5.0 E) 9.0
    Answer: E

17) What is the pH of a solution with $[OH^-] = 1 \times 10^{-4}$ M?
    A) 10.0
    B) -10.0
    C) 4.0
    D) -4.0
    E) 1.0×10^{-10}
    Answer: A

18) The $[H_3O^+]$ of a solution with pH = 2.0 is
   A) 10 M.
   B) -10 M.
   C) 1×10^2 M.
   D) 1×10^{-2} M.
   E) 1×10^{-12} M.

Answer: D

19) Which of the following is the strongest acid?

   A) H_3PO_4 B) NH_4^+ C) NaOH   D) H_2CO_3 E) HCl

Answer: E

20) A solution with $[OH^-]$ of 5×10^{-3} has a pH of _____.
   A) 2.3   B) -2.3   C) 11.7   D) 7.0   E) 5.0

Answer: C

21) The $[H_3O^+]$ of a solution with pH = 9.7 is
   A) 9.7 M.
   B) $1 \times 10^{9.7}$ M.
   C) 2×10^{-10} M.
   D) 5×10^{-5} M.
   E) 9.7×10^{-1} M.

Answer: C

22) Which of the following is correctly identified?
   A) NH_3, strong acid
   B) NaOH, strong base
   C) HCl, weak acid
   D) H_2CO_3, strong acid
   E) $Ca(OH)_2$, weak base

Answer: B

23) Ammonium hydroxide is a weak base because
   A) it is a dilute solution.
   B) it is only slightly soluble in water.
   C) it cannot hold on to its hydroxide ions.
   D) it dissociates only slightly in water.
   E) it is completely ionized in aqueous solution.

Answer: D

24) An acid and base react to form a salt and water in a(n) _____ reaction.
   A) ionization
   B) dissociation
   C) oxidation
   D) neutralization
   E) reduction

Answer: D

25) In a neutralization reaction
   A) two acids react to form water.
   B) water and a salt react to form an acid and a base.
   C) an acid and a salt react to form water and a base.
   D) a base and a salt react to form water and an acid.
   E) an acid and a base react to form a salt and water.

   Answer: E

26) Which of the following is the correctly balanced equation for the complete neutralization of H_3PO_4 with $Ca(OH)_2$?
   A) $H_3PO_4 + Ca(OH)_2 \rightarrow CaHPO_4 + 2H_2O$
   B) $3H_3PO_4 + Ca(OH)_2 \rightarrow Ca_3(PO_4)_2 + 5H_2O$
   C) $H_3PO_4 + Ca(OH)_2 \rightarrow Ca_3(PO_4)_2 + H_2O$
   D) $2H_3PO_4 + 3Ca(OH)_2 \rightarrow Ca_3(PO_4)_2 + 6H_2O$
   E) $4H_3PO_4 + 6Ca(OH)_2 \rightarrow 2Ca_3(PO_4)_2 + 12H_2O$

   Answer: D

27) The neutralization reaction between $Al(OH)_3$ and HNO_3 produces the salt with the formula
   A) H_2O.
   B) $AlNO_3$.
   C) AlH_2.
   D) $Al(NO_3)_3$.
   E) NO_3OH.

   Answer: D

28) Which of the following is a neutralization reaction?
   A) $KCl + NaNO_3 \rightarrow KNO_3 + NaCl$
   B) $HNO_3 + KOH \rightarrow H_2O + KNO_3$
   C) $H_2O + SO_3 \rightarrow H_2SO_4$
   D) $4Na + O_2 \rightarrow 2Na_2O$
   E) $2NO_2 \rightarrow 2NO + O_2$

   Answer: B

29) The function of a buffer is to
   A) change color at the end point of a titration.
   B) maintain the pH of a solution.
   C) be a strong base.
   D) maintain a neutral pH.
   E) act as a strong acid.

   Answer: B

30) The normal blood pH is about
   A) 6.8.   B) 7.0.   C) 7.2.   D) 7.4.   E) 7.6.

   Answer: D

31) In a buffer system of HF and its salt, NaF,
    A) the HF neutralizes added acid.
    B) the HF neutralizes added base.
    C) the HF is not necessary.
    D) the F^- neutralizes added H_2O.
    E) the F^- neutralizes added base.

Answer: B

32) Which of the following is a buffer system?
    A) NaCl and $NaNO_3$
    B) HCl and NaOH
    C) H_2CO_3 and $KHCO_3$
    D) NaCl and NaOH
    E) H_2O and HCl

Answer: C

33) Which of the following could be a buffer?
    A) NaF
    B) HF + NaF
    C) HF + H_2O
    D) NaF + H_2O
    E) NaCl + HF

Answer: B

34) What is the name of the medical condition of an asthmatic patient with a blood pH of 7.30?
    A) respiratory acidosis
    B) respiratory alkalosis
    C) metabolic acidosis
    D) metabolic alkalosis
    E) diabetes mellitus

Answer: A

35) If a condition of hypoventilation occurs, the blood pH of the patient is expected to
    A) saturate.
    B) increase.
    C) decrease.
    D) stay the same.
    E) concentrate.

Answer: C

36) When hyperventilation (rapid breathing) causes a patient to exhale large amounts of CO_2, the blood pH rises in a condition called
    A) metabolic acidosis.
    B) metabolic alkalosis.
    C) respiratory acidosis.
    D) respiratory alkalosis.
    E) pulmonary distress.

Answer: D

37) 25.0 mL of 0.212 M NaOH is neutralized by 13.6 mL of an HCl solution. The molarity of the NaOH solution is

A) 0.212 M.   B) 0.115 M.   C) 0.500 M.   D) 0.390 M.   E) 0.137 M.

Answer: D

38) A 10.0 mL of 0.121 M H_2SO_4 is neutralized by 17.1 mL of KOH solution. The molarity of the KOH solution is

A) 0.207 M.   B) 0.4141 M.   C) 0.0708 M.   D) 0.428 M.   E) 0.142 M.

Answer: E

8.2 True/False Questions

1) If the carbon dioxide level in the blood is too high, more carbonic acid is produced, and this results in the condition termed acidosis.

Answer: TRUE

2) Alkalosis is the blood condition in which the blood pH is higher than normal.

Answer: TRUE

3) A buffer is a solution that tends to maintain a neutral pH.

Answer: FALSE

4) In any water solution, $[H^+][OH^-] = 1.0 \times 10^{-7}$.

Answer: FALSE

5) For most reactions of acids with bases, the resulting products are a salt and water.

Answer: TRUE

6) Acids turn phenolphthalein pink.

Answer: FALSE

7) A solution with a pH greater than 7 is basic.

Answer: TRUE

8) The name of H_2SO_4 is hydrosulfuric acid.

Answer: FALSE

8.3 Matching Questions

Identify each of the following compounds as an acid, a base, or neither.

1) HCl

2) NaOH

3) NH_3

4) H_2SO_4

5) KOH

6) NaCl

7) $NaNO_3$

8) H_2CO_3

A) base

B) acid

C) neither

1) B	2) A	3) A	4) B	5) A	6) C
7) C	8) B				

In the following solutions, is the $[OH^-]$ greater than, less than, or equal to the $[H_3O^+]$?

9) acid

10) base

11) $[H_3O^+] = 1.0 \times 10^{-6}$ M

12) $[H_3O^+] = 1.0 \times 10^{-10}$ M

13) $[H_3O^+] = 1 \times 10^{-7}$ M

14) pH = 2

15) pH = 9

A) greater than

B) less than

C) equal to

9) B	10) A	11) B	12) A	13) C	14) B
15) A					

Identify the following as acids, bases, or neutral solutions.

16) has a sour taste   A) neutral

17) has a pH = 4.5   B) acid

18) turns blue litmus paper red   C) base

19) contains more hydronium
     ions than hydroxide ions

20) H_2O

21) $[H_3O^+] = 3.4 \times 10^{-5}$ M

22) $[OH^-] = 2.8 \times 10^{-2}$ M

23) $Ca(OH)_2$

24) pH = 9.0

25) $[H_3O^+] = 1.0 \times 10^{-7}$ M

| 16) B | 17) B | 18) B | 19) B | 20) A | 21) B |
| 22) C | 23) C | 24) C | 25) A | | |

Chapter 9   Nuclear Radiation

9.1   Multiple-Choice Questions

1) What is the nuclear symbol for a radioactive isotope of copper with a mass number of 60?

A) $^{60}_{29}\text{Cu}$ B) $^{29}_{60}\text{Cu}$ C) 29Cu   D) $^{60}_{31}\text{Cu}$ E) $^{31}_{29}\text{Cu}$

Answer: A

2) The product from the alpha decay of $^{235}_{92}\text{U}$ is _____.

A) $^{235}_{93}\text{Np}$ B) $^{239}_{94}\text{Pu}$ C) $^{231}_{90}\text{Th}$ D) $^{233}_{80}\text{Ra}$ E) $^{236}_{92}\text{U}$

Answer: C

3) The nuclear symbol of helium, $^{4}_{2}\text{He}$, is also the symbol for designating a(n)

A) proton.
B) neutron.
C) gamma ray.
D) beta particle.
E) alpha particle.

Answer: E

4) The symbol $^{0}_{-1}e$ is a symbol used for a(n)

A) proton.
B) neutron.
C) gamma ray.
D) beta particle.
E) alpha particle.

Answer: D

5) Which of the following types of radiation has the highest energy?
A) α-particles
B) β-particles
C) γ-rays
D) visible light
E) All of these have the same energy.

Answer: C

6) The damaging effects of radiation on the body are a result of
A) the formation of unstable ions or radicals.
B) the formation of radioactive atoms in the body.
C) transmutation reactions in the body.
D) extensive damage to nerve cells.
E) the production of radioactive sodium ions in the body.

Answer: A

7) Which of the following is suitable as a minimum shielding for beta particles?
   A) air
   B) 1 m of water
   C) gloves
   D) 1 m of concrete
   E) 1 cm of lead

Answer: C

8) For $^{85}_{38}$Sr, there are

   A) 85 protons and 38 neutrons.
   B) 47 protons and 38 neutrons.
   C) 38 protons and 47 neutrons.
   D) 38 protons and 85 neutrons.
   E) 85 protons and 47 neutrons.

Answer: C

9) Which is NOT a way to minimize your exposure to radiation?
   A) wearing a lead apron
   B) keeping a good distance
   C) standing behind a thick concrete wall
   D) wearing lead-lined gloves
   E) staying a longer time

Answer: E

10) The process in which a nucleus spontaneously breaks down by emitting radiation is known as
    A) transformation.
    B) translation.
    C) fusion.
    D) a chain reaction.
    E) radioactive decay.

Answer: E

11) A nuclear equation is balanced when
    A) the same elements are found on both sides of the equation.
    B) the sum of the mass numbers and the sum of the atomic numbers of the particles and atoms are the same on both sides of the equation.
    C) the same particles and atoms are on both sides of the equation.
    D) different particles and atoms are on both sides of the equation.
    E) the charges of the particles and atoms are the same on both sides of the equation.

Answer: B

12) The nuclear reaction shown below is an example of what type of process?

$$^{224}_{90}\text{Th} \rightarrow ^{220}_{88}\text{Rn} + ^{4}_{2}\text{He}$$

A) fusion
B) fission
C) translation
D) alpha emission
E) beta emission

Answer: D

13) In the nuclear equation of a beta emitter,
   A) the new nucleus contains 2 fewer protons.
   B) the new nucleus contains 2 more protons.
   C) the mass number of the new nucleus is 4 less than that of the original nucleus.
   D) the new nucleus contains 1 more proton.
   E) the new nucleus contains 1 less proton.

Answer: D

14) Nitrogen–17 is a beta emitter. What is the isotope produced in the radioactive decay?

A) $^{18}_{6}\text{C}$ B) $^{13}_{5}\text{B}$ C) $^{18}_{7}\text{N}$ D) $^{13}_{9}\text{F}$ E) $^{17}_{8}\text{O}$

Answer: E

15) The nuclear reaction

$$^{126}_{50}\text{Sn} \rightarrow ^{126}_{51}\text{Sb} + ?$$

is an example of
   A) fusion.
   B) fission.
   C) gamma emission.
   D) alpha emission.
   E) beta emission.

Answer: E

16) What is the radioactive particle released in the following nuclear equation?

$$^{90}_{38}\text{Sr} \rightarrow ^{90}_{39}\text{Y} + ?$$

A) alpha particle
B) beta particle
C) gamma ray
D) proton
E) neutron

Answer: B

17) What is the radioactive particle released in the following nuclear equation?

$$^{159}_{74}\text{W} \rightarrow \, ^{155}_{72}\text{Hf} + \, ?$$

A) alpha particle
B) beta particle
C) gamma ray
D) proton
E) neutron

Answer: A

18) The nuclear symbol that completes the equation is a(n)

$$^{240}_{95}\text{Am} + \, ? \rightarrow \, ^{243}_{97}\text{Bk} + \, ^{1}_{0}\text{n}$$

A) proton.
B) neutron.
C) gamma ray.
D) beta particle.
E) alpha particle.

Answer: E

19) The nuclear symbol that completes the equation is a(n)

$$^{58}_{26}\text{Fe} + \, ? \rightarrow \, ^{59}_{26}\text{Fe}$$

A) proton.
B) neutron.
C) gamma ray.
D) beta particle.
E) alpha particle.

Answer: B

20) What is the radiation particle used in the bombardment of nitrogen-14?

$$^{14}_{7}\text{N} + \, ? \rightarrow \, ^{14}_{6}\text{C} + \, ^{1}_{1}\text{H}$$

A) alpha particle
B) beta particle
C) gamma ray
D) proton
E) neutron

Answer: E

21) When aluminum-27 is bombarded with a neutron, a gamma ray is emitted. What radioactive isotope is produced?
   A) silicon-27
   B) silicon-28
   C) aluminum-28
   D) magnesium-27
   E) magnesium-28

   Answer: C

22) The unit used to measure the amount of radiation absorbed by a gram of material is called the
   A) rad.   B) RBE.   C) curie.   D) rem.   E) Bq.

   Answer: A

23) A patient receives 4×10^3 mrads of iodine-131, which emits β-particles. If the factor that adjusts for biological damage is 1 for β-particles, how many rems did the patient receive?
   A) 4   B) 0.4   C) 0.3   D) 2   E) 40

   Answer: A

24) A patient receives 10 mrads of gamma radiation. If the factor that adjusts for biological damage for for gamma radiation is 1, how many mrems did the patient receive?
   A) 2 mrem
   B) 5 mrem
   C) 10 mrem
   D) 20 mrem
   E) 200 mrem

   Answer: C

25) Why is it important that radioisotopes used in diagnostic tests have short half-lives?
   A) These radioisotopes have a greater activity so they are easier to monitor.
   B) This minimizes the harmful side effects of the radiation.
   C) This is necessary so the radioisotopes will have high energy.
   D) These radioisotopes are less expensive.
   E) These radioisotopes are more abundant in nature.

   Answer: B

26) A person begins to suffer radiation sickness at an exposure level of
   A) 25 rem.   B) 5 rem.   C) 500 rem.   D) 100 rem.   E) 600 rem.

   Answer: D

27) A positron is a particle emitted from the nucleus that has the same mass as a(n)
   A) electron but has a positive charge.
   B) neutron but has a positive charge.
   C) alpha particle.
   D) beta particle.
   E) proton emitted from the nucleus.

   Answer: A

28) An imaging technique in which a computer monitors the degree of absorption of X-ray beams is known as
    A) positron emission tomography (PET).
    B) magnetic resonance imaging (MRI).
    C) computerized tomography (CT).
    D) radioactive iodine uptake (RAIU).
    E) a scan.

Answer: C

29) An imaging technique that detects the energy emitted by hydrogen atoms in a magnetic field is known as
    A) positron emission tomography (PET).
    B) computerized tomography (CT).
    C) magnetic resonance imaging (MRI).
    D) radioactive tracer study.
    E) supermagnetic tomography (SMT).

Answer: C

30) The dosage of technetium-99m for myocardial imaging is 280 μCi/kg of body weight. How many mCi should be given to a patient weighing 65 kg?
    A) 0.0043 mCi
    B) 4.3 mCi
    C) 18 mCi
    D) 230 mCi
    E) 1.8×10^4 mCi

Answer: C

31) A patient receives 3.0 mL of a solution containing technetium-99m for a breast image. If the activity of the technetium-99m is 9.5 mCi/mL, what is the dose received by the patient?
    A) 3.2 mCi   B) 29 mCi   C) 320 μCi   D) 9.5 mCi   E) 28.5 mCi

Answer: B

32) Sodium-24 has a half-life of 15 hours. How many hours is three half-lives?
    A) 60 hours   B) 45 hours   C) 30 hours   D) 15 hours   E) 7.5 hours

Answer: B

33) The half-life of a radioisotope is
    A) one-half of the time it takes for the radioisotope to completely decay to a nonradioactive isotope.
    B) the time it takes for the radioisotope to become an isotope with one-half of the atomic weight of the original radioisotope.
    C) the time it takes for the radioisotope to become an isotope with one-half the atomic number of the original radioisotope.
    D) the time it takes for the radioisotope to lose one-half of its neutrons.
    E) the time it takes for one-half of the sample to decay.

Answer: E

34) Iodine-123, which is used for diagnostic imaging in the thyroid, has a half-life of 13 hours. If 50.0 mg of I-123 were prepared at 8:00 A.M. on Monday, how many mg remain at 10:00 A.M. on the following day?
    A) 50.0 mg   B) 25.0 mg   C) 12.5 mg   D) 6.25 mg   E) 3.13 mg
    Answer: C

35) A wooden object from a prehistoric site has a carbon-14 activity of 10 counts per minute (cpm) compared to 40 cpm for new wood. If carbon-14 has a half-life of 5730 years, what is the age of the wood?
    A) 1430 yr   B) 5730 yr   C) 11,500 yr   D) 17,200 yr   E) 22,900 yr
    Answer: C

36) Krypton-79 has a half-life of 35 hours. How many half-lives have passed after 105 hours?
    A) 1 half-life
    B) 2 half-lives
    C) 3 half-lives
    D) 4 half-lives
    E) 5 half-lives
    Answer: C

37) The half-life of bromine-74 is 25 min. How much of a 4.0 mg sample is still active after 75 min?
    A) 0.50 mg   B) 1.0 mg   C) 2.0 mg   D) 0.25 mg   E) 4.0 mg
    Answer: A

38) When an atom of uranium-235 is bombarded with neutrons, it splits into smaller nuclei and produces a great amount of energy. This nuclear process is called
    A) fission.
    B) fusion.
    C) decomposition.
    D) chain reaction.
    E) ionization.
    Answer: A

39) In the sun, nuclei of hydrogen combine to form a larger nucleus and release a great amount of energy. The process is known as
    A) fission.
    B) fusion.
    C) metathesis.
    D) chain reaction.
    E) ionization.
    Answer: B

40) Gamma rays require the heaviest shielding of all the common types of nuclear radiation because gamma rays have the
    A) highest energy.
    B) most intense color.
    C) lowest energy.
    D) largest particles.
    E) heaviest particles.
    Answer: A

41) If absorbed internally, alpha particle emitters are the most damaging because alpha particles
    A) have the largest charge.
    B) have the greatest energy.
    C) have the greatest mass.
    D) consist of high energy electrons.
    E) consist of pure energy.

Answer: C

42) Radium-226 decays by alpha emission to
    A) barium-131.
    B) cobalt-60.
    C) carbon-14.
    D) polonium-218.
    E) radon-222.

Answer: E

43) A sample of cerium-141 for a diagnostic test was dissolved in saline solution to an activity of 4.5 millicuries/mL. If the patient undergoing the test needs a dose of 10 millicuries, how much of the solution should be injected into the patient?
    A) 45 mL   B) .45 mL   C) 2.2 mL   D) 22 mL   E) 4.5 mL

Answer: C

44) The most widely used medical isotope in nuclear medicine is
    A) Tc-99m.   B) I-131.   C) P-32.   D) I-125.   E) Co-60.

Answer: A

45) The recommended dosage of I-131 for a test is 4.2 microcuries per kg of body weight. How many millicuries should be given to a 55 kg patient? (1 mCi = 1000 μCi)
    A) 230 millicuries
    B) 0.23 millicuries
    C) 0.076 millicuries
    D) 760 millicuries
    E) 13.8 millicuries

Answer: B

46) A radiation lab orders 64 μCi of P-32. After 42 days the activity of the sample is 8.0 μCi. What is the half-life of P-32?
    A) 7 days   B) 14 days   C) 28 days   D) 42 days   E) 84 days

Answer: B

47) A sample of I-131 decays from 12 microcuries to 3.0 microcuries in 16 days. What is the half-life of I-131?
    A) 16 days   B) 8 days   C) 32 days   D) 64 days   E) 4 days

Answer: B

48) One symptom of mild radiation sickness is
   A) a lowered white cell count.
   B) a raised white cell count.
   C) a lowered red blood cell count.
   D) a raised red blood cell count.
   E) a white cell count of zero.

   Answer: A

9.2 Short Answer Questions

1) One symbol for the β particle is $_{-1}^{0}\beta$. Another symbol for the same particle is _____.

   Answer: $_{-1}^{0}e$

2) The common unit of radioactivity which is used to measure the biological damage is the _____.

   Answer: rem

3) The radioisotope used as a diagnostic tool to measure thyroid function is _____.

   Answer: I-131

4) The diagnostic imaging technique that depends on magnetic fields and radio waves, not radioactivity, is called _____.

   Answer: MRI or magnetic resonance imaging

5) The time needed for a radioactive sample to decay to one-half of its original activity is called the _____.

   Answer: half-life

6) There are _____ microcuries in one millicurie.

   Answer: 1000

7) In alpha emission, the atomic number _____.

   Answer: decreases by two

8) In beta emission, the atomic number _____.

   Answer: increases by one

9) If a neutron is lost from a nucleus, the atomic number _____.

   Answer: does not change

10) $_{92}^{235}U + _{0}^{1}n \rightarrow$ _____ $+ _{36}^{91}Kr + 3_{0}^{1}n + energy$

   Answer: $_{56}^{142}Ba$

11) The radiation dose required to produce death in one-half of the exposed subject animals is termed the _____.

   Answer: LD_{50}

12) $^{99m}_{43}\text{Tc} \rightarrow ^{99}_{43}\text{Tc} +$ _____

Answer: γ

9.3 True/False Questions

1) Exposure to radiation is unavoidable because some radioactive elements occur naturally.

Answer: TRUE

2) One symptom of radiation sickness is an increased production of red blood cells.

Answer: FALSE

3) If the half-life of hydrogen-3 is 11.8 years, after two half-lives the radioactivity of a sample will be reduced to one-half of the original amount.

Answer: FALSE

4) The correct symbol for hydrogen-3 is $^{3}_{2}\text{He}$.

Answer: FALSE

5) One mCi of a radioactive substance emits more radiation than one μCi of the same substance.

Answer: TRUE

6) One type of radiation that is not used for medical procedures is the cosmic ray.

Answer: TRUE

7) X rays are generated by the nucleus during radioactive decay.

Answer: FALSE

8) Irradiation of food for sterilization is usually carried out using gamma irradiation.

Answer: TRUE

9) During alpha emission, the atomic number decreases.

Answer: TRUE

10) When beta particles are emitted, the atomic number decreases.

Answer: FALSE

11) Nuclear fission as used in nuclear power plants produces radioactive waste with long half-lives.

Answer: TRUE

12) The production of nitrogen-13 and a neutron from boron-10 by bombardment with a helium-4 nucleus is an example of radioactive decay.

Answer: FALSE

9.4 Matching Questions

Indicate whether each of the following is characteristic of the fission or fusion process.

1) A large nucleus is split into smaller nuclei.

2) Very high temperatures must be achieved to initiate the reaction.

3) This nuclear process provides the energy of the sun.

4) This process produces radioactive by–products.

5) Large amounts of energy are released.

6) Two small nuclei combine to form a larger nucleus.

A) fission

B) fusion

C) both fission and fusion

1) A   2) B   3) B   4) A   5) C   6) B

Choose the type of radiation from Column 2 that best matches each item in Column 1.

7) α

8) β

9) γ

10) $_{1}^{1}H$

11) $_{0}^{1}n$

A) beta particle

B) proton

C) gamma ray

D) alpha particle

E) neutron

7) D   8) A   9) C   10) B   11) E

Chapter 10 Introduction to Organic Chemistry: Alkanes

10.1 Multiple-Choice Questions

1) Compounds that have the same molecular formula but different arrangements of atoms are called
   A) isomers.
   B) isotopes.
   C) indicators.
   D) isozymes.
   E) isometrics.

Answer: A

2) Which of the following is true of nonane, C_9H_{20}, which has a density of 0.79 g/mL, melts at
   –51 °C, and boils at 157 °C?
   A) Nonane is soluble in water.
   B) Nonane is a gas at room temperature.
   C) Nonane is a solid at room temperature.
   D) Nonane does not undergo combustion.
   E) Nonane floats on the surface of water.

Answer: E

3) A formula that shows the arrangement of all bonds in a molecule is called a(n)
   A) molecular formula.
   B) expanded structural formula.
   C) condensed structural formula.
   D) condensed molecular formula.
   E) isomeric formula.

Answer: B

4) In the three-dimensional structure of methane, CH_4, the hydrogen atoms attached to a carbon
   atom are aligned
   A) in a straight line.
   B) at the corners of a square.
   C) at the corners of a tetrahedron.
   D) at the corners of a rectangle.
   E) at the corners of a cube.

Answer: C

5) A hydrocarbon contains only the elements
   A) hydrogen and oxygen.
   B) carbon and oxygen.
   C) carbon and hydrogen.
   D) carbon, hydrogen, and oxygen.
   E) carbon, hydrogen, and nitrogen.

Answer: C

6) The functional group contained in the compound CH_3-CH_2-OH is a(n)
   A) aldehyde.
   B) alkene.
   C) alcohol.
   D) ketone.
   E) ether.

Answer: C

7) What type of compound is $CH_3-CH_2-CH_3$?
   A) alkane
   B) branched alkane
   C) cycloalkane
   D) haloalkane
   E) isomer

Answer: A

8) What is the name of this compound?

$$\begin{array}{c} Cl \\ | \\ CH_3 - C\,H - CH_2 - CH_2 - Cl \end{array}$$

   A) 1,1-dichlorobutane
   B) 1,2,-dichlorobutane
   C) 1,3-dichlorobutane
   D) 1,4-dichlorobutane
   E) dichlorobutane

Answer: C

9) The special feature that determines the family name and chemical reactivity of the organic compound it is found in is called a(n)
   A) functional group.
   B) organic compound.
   C) identifying group.
   D) ionic bond.
   E) covalent bond.

Answer: A

10) Which of the following is NOT typical of most organic compounds?
    A) high melting point
    B) poor solubility in water
    C) low boiling point
    D) covalent bonding
    E) high flammability

Answer: A

11) A functional group is a certain group of atoms that
    A) increases water solubility.
    B) reacts in a predictable way whenever present.
    C) changes the color of the molecule whenever present.
    D) always contains oxygen or nitrogen.
    E) never contains a halogen.

Answer: B

12) An alkene is a carbon compound that contains a _____ bond.
    A) single   B) double   C) triple   D) aromatic   E) hydrogen

Answer: B

13) An alkyne is a carbon compound that contains a _____ bond.
    A) single   B) double   C) triple   D) aromatic   E) hydrogen

Answer: C

$$\overset{\displaystyle O}{\overset{\displaystyle \|}{}}$$

14) The functional group contained in the compound CH_3-C-H is a(n)
    A) aldehyde.
    B) alkene.
    C) alcohol.
    D) ketone.
    E) ether.

Answer: A

15) The functional group contained in the compound $CH_3-CH_2-O-CH_2-CH_3$ is a(n)
    A) aldehyde.
    B) alkene.
    C) alcohol.
    D) ketone.
    E) ether.

Answer: E

$$\overset{\displaystyle O}{\overset{\displaystyle \|}{}}$$

16) The functional group contained in the compound $CH_3-CH_2-C-NH_2$ is a(n)
    A) thiol.
    B) carboxylic acid.
    C) amine.
    D) ester.
    E) amide.

Answer: E

17) The functional group contained in the compound $CH_3-CH_2-CH=CH-CH_3$ is a(n)
    A) aldehyde.
    B) alkene.
    C) alcohol.
    D) ketone.
    E) ether.

Answer: B

18) The functional group contained in the compound $CH_3-CH_2-\overset{\overset{\textstyle O}{\textstyle \|}}{C}-O-CH_3$ is a(n)
   A) thiol.
   B) carboxylic acid.
   C) amine.
   D) ester.
   E) amide.

   Answer: D

19) The functional group contained in the compound $CH_3-CH_2-\overset{\overset{\textstyle O}{\textstyle \|}}{C}-O-H$ is a(n)
   A) thiol.
   B) carboxylic acid.
   C) amine.
   D) ester.
   E) amide.

   Answer: B

20) The functional group contained in the compound $CH_3-CH_2-NH_2$ is a(n)
   A) thiol.
   B) carboxylic acid.
   C) amine.
   D) ester.
   E) amide.

   Answer: C

21) Isomers are molecules that share the same formula and have
   A) a different shape to the molecule.
   B) the same arrangement of atoms within the molecule.
   C) a different arrangement of atoms within the molecule.
   D) identical boiling points.
   E) the same shape in each molecule.

   Answer: C

22) Organic chemistry is the study of the chemistry of compounds of
   A) oxygen.
   B) hydrogen.
   C) living things.
   D) polymers.
   E) carbon.

   Answer: E

23) How does a molecule of a vitamin synthesized in the laboratory behave when compared to the behavior of the same vitamin isolated from a natural source (e.g., vitamin C synthesized, compared to vitamin C from rose hips)?
   A) identical in every way
   B) usually identical
   C) some effects are the same
   D) few effects are the same
   E) The natural vitamin is better.

Answer: A

24) How many valence electrons does carbon have?
   A) one   B) two   C) three   D) four   E) five

Answer: D

25) Carbon atoms always have how many covalent bonds?
   A) one   B) two   C) three   D) four   E) five

Answer: D

26) Hydrocarbons are the primary constituents of
   A) drugs.
   B) food flavors.
   C) fossil fuels.
   D) fruit juices.
   E) disinfectants.

Answer: C

27) Identify the functional group in the compound CH_3–CH_2–SH.
   A) amide
   B) ketone
   C) ester
   D) secondary amine
   E) thiol

Answer: E

28) In an amine functional group, the central atom is
   A) carbon.
   B) hydrogen.
   C) oxygen.
   D) nitrogen.
   E) sulfur.

Answer: D

29) The carbon atoms in saturated hydrocarbons
   A) have only single bonds.
   B) contain at least one double bond.
   C) contain at least one triple bond.
   D) contain a benzene ring.
   E) contain both a double and a triple bond.

Answer: A

30) An organic compound composed of carbon and hydrogen connected only by single bonds is an
   A) alkane.
   B) alkene.
   C) alkyne.
   D) aromatic compound.
   E) alcohol.

Answer: A

31) Which of these formulas is the expanded structural formula for an alkane with three carbon atoms?

   A) C_3H_6

   B) C_3H_8

   C) $CH_3- CH_2- CH_3$

   D) C – C – C

   E)   H   H   H
         | | |
      H – C – C – C – H
         | | |
         H   H   H

Answer: E

32) What is the condensed structural formula for an alkane with four carbon atoms?
   A) $CH_3-CH=CH-CH_3$
   B) $CH_3-CH_2-CH_2-CH_3$
   C) C_4H_{10}
   D) C – C – C – C
   E)   H   H   H   H
         | | | |
      H – C – C – C – C – H
         | | | |
         H   H   H   H

Answer: B

33) What is the name of the continuous chain alkane with six carbon atoms?
   A) butane   B) pentane   C) hexane   D) heptane   E) octane

Answer: C

34) What is the name of this compound?

   $CH_3- CH_2- CH_2- CH_2- CH_2- CH_2- CH_3$

   A) hexane   B) heptane   C) octane   D) butane   E) pentane

Answer: B

35) What is the name of this compound?

$$CH_3-CH_2-CH_2-CH_2-CH_3$$

    A) pentane
    B) hexane
    C) heptane
    D) octane
    E) methylbutane

Answer: A

36) What is the name of $CH_3-CH_2-CH_2-CH_3$?
        A) ethane   B) propane   C) butane   D) pentane   E) hexane
Answer: C

37) The reaction of butane with oxygen is called
        A) substitution.
        B) addition.
        C) neutralization.
        D) combustion.
        E) titration.

Answer: D

38) What is(are) the product(s) of the complete combustion of any hydrocarbon?
        A) CO only
        B) CO_2 only
        C) $CO + H_2O$
        D) $CO_2 + H_2O$
        E) H_2O only

Answer: D

39) The balanced equation for the complete combustion of C_5H_{12} will give which of these
    product(s)?
        A) CO_2 only
        B) $C_5H_{12}O_5$ only
        C) $5CO_2 + 5H_2O$
        D) $5CO_2 + 6H_2O$
        E) $10CO + 12H_2O$

Answer: D

40) What is the name of the alkyl group $CH_3-CH_2-CH_2-$?
        A) propane   B) methyl   C) ethane   D) ethyl   E) propyl
Answer: E

41) What is the IUPAC name for this alkane?

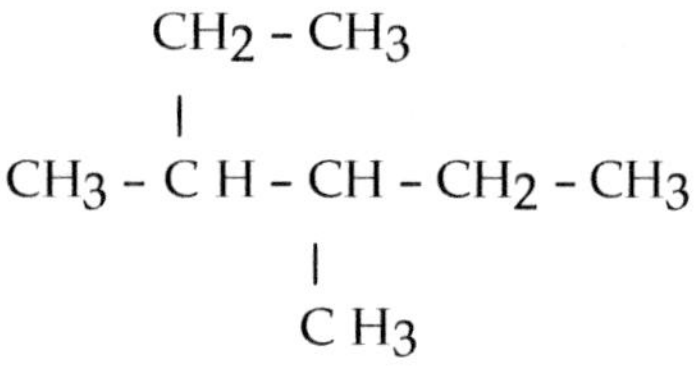

$$CH_2 - CH_3$$
$$|$$
$$CH_3 - C H - CH - CH_2 - CH_3$$
$$|$$
$$C H_3$$

   A) 2-ethyl-3-methylpentane
   B) 4-ethyl-3-methylpentane
   C) 3, 4-dimethylhexane
   D) 2, 3-diethylbutane
   E) octane

Answer: C

42) What is the IUPAC name of this alkane?

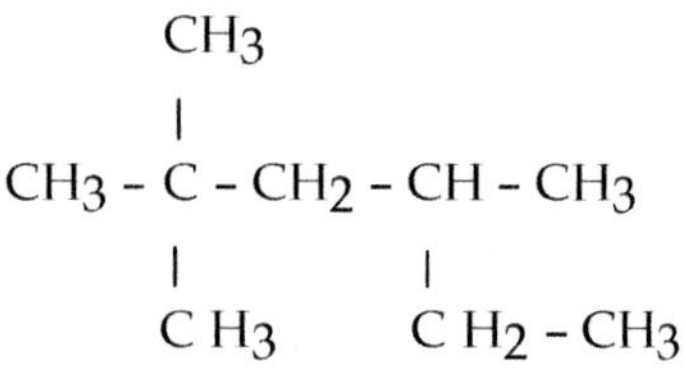

$$CH_3$$
$$|$$
$$CH_3 - C - CH_2 - CH - CH_3$$
$$|$$
$$C H_3 \qquad C H_2 - CH_3$$

   A) 4-ethyl-2,2-dimethylpentane
   B) 2-ethyl-4,4-dimethylpentane
   C) 2,2,4-trimethylhexane
   D) 2-ethyl-2,2-dimethylpentane
   E) 3,5,5-trimethylhexane

Answer: C

43) Which of the following compounds could have the molecular formula C_7H_{16}?
   A) hexane
   B) pentane
   C) 2-methylheptane
   D) 2,3-dimethylpentane
   E) 3-ethylhexane

Answer: D

44) What is the name of 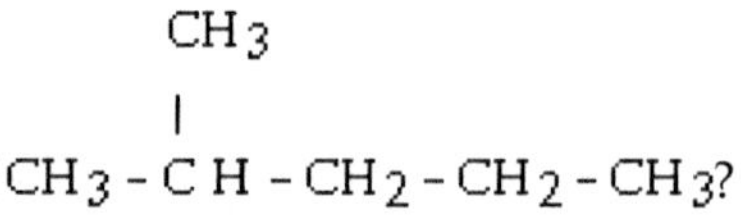
$$CH_3$$
$$|$$
$$CH_3 - C H - CH_2 - CH_2 - CH_3?$$
   A) pentane
   B) methylpentane
   C) 2-methylpentane
   D) 4-methylpentane
   E) hexane

Answer: C

45) What is the name of

$$CH_3 - \overset{\overset{\displaystyle CH_3}{\displaystyle |}}{\underset{\underset{\displaystyle CH_3}{\displaystyle |}}{C}} - CH_2 - CH_3?$$

   A) hexane
   B) dimethylbutane
   C) 3,3–dimethylbutane
   D) 2,2–dimethylbutane
   E) 2–dimethylbutane

   Answer: D

46) Which of the following pairs of formulas represent isomers?

   A) $CH_3 - CH_2$ and $CH_3 - CH_2 - CH_2$
       | |
       $CH_2{-}CH_3$ CH_3

   B) $CH_3 - CH_2 - CH_2 - CH_3$ and $CH_3 - CH_2 - CH_3$

   C) CH_3
               |
        $CH_3 - C - CH_3$ and $CH_3 - CH_2 - CH_3$
               |
             CH_3

   D) CH_3 CH_3 CH_3
       | | |
      $CH_2 - CH$ and $CH_3 - CH_2 - CH - CH_3$
               |
             CH_3

   E) CH_3 CH_3
             | |
      $CH_3 - CH - CH - CH_3$ and $CH_3 - CH_2 - C - CH_3$
               | |
             CH_3 CH_3

   Answer: E

47) A cycloalkane
   A) has two fewer carbon atoms than the corresponding alkane.
   B) has two fewer hydrogen atoms than the corresponding alkane.
   C) contains – CH_3 groups joined by single bonds.
   D) always contains a three carbon ring.
   E) has no hydrogen atoms.

   Answer: B

48) The simplest cycloalkane has
   A) one carbon atom.
   B) two carbon atoms.
   C) three carbon atoms.
   D) four carbon atoms
   E) five carbon atoms.

Answer: C

49) The reaction for the combustion of heptane is

$$C_7H_{16} + 11O_2 \rightarrow 7CO_2 + 8H_2O.$$

How many liters of CO_2 at STP are produced from the complete combustion of 2.00 moles of heptane?
   A) 44.8 L   B) 22.4 L   C) 157 L   D) 246 L   E) 314 L

Answer: E

50) What is the name for a one-carbon alkyl substituent?
   A) methyl   B) ethyl   C) propyl   D) butyl   E) pentyl

Answer: A

51) What is the name for a two-carbon saturated alkyl group?
   A) methyl   B) ethyl   C) propyl   D) butyl   E) pentyl

Answer: B

52) What is the name for a three-carbon saturated alkyl group?
   A) methyl   B) ethyl   C) propyl   D) butyl   E) pentyl

Answer: C

53) What is the name for this three-carbon alkyl group?

$$CH_3 -CH-CH_3$$
$$|$$

   A) *n*-propyl
   B) *iso*-propyl
   C) butyl
   D) *iso*-butyl
   E) ethyl

Answer: B

54) What is the name for a four-carbon continuous-chain alkane?
   A) methane   B) ethane   C) propane   D) butane   E) pentane

Answer: D

55) What is the name for a five-carbon continuous-chain alkane?
   A) methane   B) ethane   C) propane   D) butane   E) pentane

Answer: E

56) What is the mame for a six-carbon continuous–chain alkane?
    A) hexane   B) heptane   C) octane   D) nonane   E) decane

Answer: A

57) What is the name for a seven-carbon continuous-chain alkane?
    A) hexane   B) heptane   C) octane   D) nonane   E) decane

Answer: B

58) What is the name for an eight-carbon continuous-chain alkane?
    A) hexane   B) heptane   C) octane   D) nonane   E) decane

Answer: C

59) What is the name of the nine-carbon continuous-chain alkane?
    A) hexane   B) heptane   C) octane   D) nonane   E) decane

Answer: D

60) What is the name for a ten-carbon continuous–chain alkane?
    A) hexane   B) heptane   C) octane   D) nonane   E) decane

Answer: E

61) In a condensed structural formula, each carbon atom is
    A) shown with all individual atoms and bonds drawn.
    B) shown with only the other carbon atoms.
    C) grouped with its bonded hydrogen atoms.
    D) not explicitly shown.
    E) written in lowercase letters.

Answer: C

62) According to the IUPAC convention for chemical naming, which part of a hydrocarbon is selected as the main chain for a hydrocarbon chain?
    A) the most highly branched chain
    B) the shortest chain
    C) the longest chain drawn in a straight line
    D) the longest continuous chain, regardless of bends
    E) the chain with the most substituted carbons in it

Answer: D

63) According to the IUPAC convention, alkyl group names should be located _____ of the name of the main chain.
    A) in front   B) at the end   C) in the middle

Answer: A

64) According to the IUPAC convention, alkyl substituents on a hydrocarbon chain should be listed in which order?
    A) alphabetical including prefixes
    B) alphabetical without considering prefixes
    C) in order with the substituent having the highest number of carbons first
    D) in order with the substituent having the lowest number of carbons first
    E) in order with the substituent having the highest total number of carbons first

Answer: B

65) When drawing a structural formula, the first step is to draw
   A) the substituents.
   B) the most highly substituted carbons.
   C) the saturated carbons.
   D) the main carbon chain.
   E) the functional group.

Answer: D

66) What functional group(s) present in the following compound?

$$HO-CH_2-CH_2-\overset{\overset{\displaystyle O}{\|}}{C}-OH$$

   A) alcohol
   B) aldehyde
   C) carboxylic acid
   D) alcohol and aldehyde
   E) alcohol and carboxylic acid

Answer: E

67) What is the name of the following compound?

$$CH_3-CH_2-CH_2-CH_2-\overset{\overset{\displaystyle CH_3}{|}}{CH}-CH_3$$

   A) heptane
   B) methylhexane
   C) 5-methylhexane
   D) 2-methylhexane
   E) 2-methylpentane

Answer: D

68) What functional group(s) are present in the following compound?

$$H_2N-CH_2-\overset{\overset{\displaystyle O}{\|}}{C}-CH_3$$

   A) amine
   B) amide
   C) ketone
   D) amine and ketone
   E) amine and carboxylic acid

Answer: D

10.2 True/False Questions

1) Organic chemistry is the study of the chemistry of carbon compounds.
   Answer: TRUE

2) Nylon, polyester, and most other plastics are carbon compounds.
   Answer: TRUE

3) Lipids are not organic compounds.
   Answer: FALSE

4) There are millions of organic compounds.
   Answer: TRUE

5) Carbon has six valence electrons.
   Answer: FALSE

6) Methane has a tetrahedral structure.
   Answer: TRUE

7) Organic compounds are always highly water soluble.
   Answer: FALSE

8) Most organic compounds are flammable.
   Answer: TRUE

9) Isomers have the same molecular formula.
   Answer: TRUE

10) Organic compounds usually have low melting and boiling points.
    Answer: TRUE

11) Organic liquids are often lighter than water.
    Answer: TRUE

12) Organic compounds usually contain carbon, hydrogen and metal atoms.
    Answer: FALSE

13) Most prescription drugs are organic molecules.
    Answer: TRUE

14) Functional groups are groups of atoms that act in predictable ways.
    Answer: TRUE

15) Functional groups always contain atoms other than just carbon and hydrogen.
    Answer: FALSE

16) Organic compounds can only be made by living things because a "vital force" is needed for their creation.
    Answer: FALSE

17) When naming an alkane, the main chain is the longest continuous carbon chain regardless of bends.
    Answer: TRUE

18) Octane is a seven carbon linear alkane.
    Answer: FALSE

19) The first four linear alkyl substituent groups are named methyl, ethyl, propyl, and butyl.
    Answer: TRUE

20) Mineral oil is a liquid hydrocarbon used as a laxative and lubricant in medical practice.
    Answer: TRUE

21) Solid alkanes are found on the surface of many fruits and vegetables.

Answer: TRUE

22) Hexane has six carbon atoms.

Answer: TRUE

23) $CH_3-CH_2-\overset{\overset{\displaystyle O}{\|}}{C}-H$ has a carboxylic acid functional group.

Answer: FALSE

10.3 Matching Questions

Identify the following as more characteristic of an organic compound or an inorganic compound.

    1) high melting point   A) organic

    2) flammable   B) inorganic

    3) covalent bonds

    4) contains metal atoms

    5) insoluble in water

    6) ionic bonds

1) B   2) A   3) A   4) B   5) A   6) B

Match the following organic structures with the appropriate family name.

7) CH$_3$-CH$_2$-CH=CH$_2$ A) alkene

8)   O   B) carboxylic acid
          ‖
     CH$_3$ – C – CH$_3$ C) alcohol

          D) ester

9) CH$_3$-OH   E) alkyne

10)   O   F) amine
          ‖
     CH$_3$-CH$_2$ –C –O-H   G) aldehyde

11) CH$_3$-CH$_2$-O-CH$_2$-CH$_3$ H) ether

12)   O   I) ketone
          ‖
     CH$_3$– C –O-CH$_2$-CH$_3$

13)   O
          ‖
     CH$_3$-CH$_2$ –C –H

14) HC≡CCH$_3$

15) CH$_3$-CH$_2$-NH$_2$

7) A   8) I   9) C   10) B   11) H   12) D
13) G   14) E   15) F

Chapter 11   Unsaturated Hydrocarbons

11.1   Multiple-Choice Questions

1) A hydrocarbon with a double bond is a(n)
   A) alkane.
   B) alkene.
   C) alkyne.
   D) alcohol.
   E) saturated compound.

   Answer: B

2) Alkenes and alkynes are called unsaturated compounds because
   A) they have the maximum number of hydrogen atoms attached to each carbon in the compound.
   B) they have fewer hydrogen atoms attached to the carbon chain than alkanes.
   C) they have more hydrogen atoms attached to the carbon chain than alkanes.
   D) they have more carbon atoms than alkanes.
   E) they have fewer carbon atoms than alkanes.

   Answer: B

3) Which of the compounds is a cycloalkene?
   A) $CH_2 = CH-CH = CH_2$

   B)

   C) $CH_3-CH = CH_2$
   D)

   E)

   Answer: D

4) An unsaturated compound always
   A) is a cycloalkane.
   B) contains a double bond.
   C) contains a triple bond.
   D) contains at least one double or triple bond.
   E) is aromatic.

   Answer: D

5) Which of the following compounds is an alkyne?
   A) $CH_3-CH_2-CH_3$
   B) C_3H_6
   C) $CH_3-CH_2-C\equiv CH$
   D) $H_2C=CH-CH=CH_2$
   E) 2-pentene

   Answer: C

6) Organic compounds with double or triple bonds are classified as
   A) unsaturated compounds.
   B) saturated compounds.
   C) dilute solutions.
   D) concentrated solutions.
   E) substituted compounds.

   Answer: A

7) The IUPAC name of $CH_3-CH=CH-CH_3$ is
   A) 2-butene.
   B) 2-butane.
   C) 1-butene.
   D) butene.
   E) 2-butyne.

   Answer: A

8) When naming an alkene, the parent chain is the longest carbon chain
   A) that does not contain the double bond.
   B) regardless of whether or not it contains the double bond.
   C) that contains at least one of the carbon atoms of the double bond.
   D) that contains both atoms of the double bond.
   E) that contains a branch.

   Answer: D

9) The IUPAC name for $CH_3-CH_2-C\equiv C-CH_3$ is
   A) 3-pentyne.
   B) 2-pentyne.
   C) pentyne.
   D) 1-methylbutyne.
   E) 2-propene.

   Answer: B

10) The IUPAC name for ethylene is
    A) ethane.
    B) cycloethane.
    C) ethyne.
    D) ethanene.
    E) ethene.

Answer: E

11) Which one of the following compounds has the smallest number of hydrogen atoms?
    A) butyne.
    B) 2–methylpropane.
    C) butene.
    D) 2–methylcyclopropane.
    E) butane.

Answer: A

12) What is the IUPAC name for the following compound?

$$CH_3-CH-C-CH=CH$$

with CH_3 and Cl substituents above, and CH_3 and CH_3 below

    A) 4–chloro–4,5–dimethyl–2–hexene
    B) 3–chloro–1,3,4–trimethyl–1–pentene
    C) 3–chloro–2,3–dimethyl–4–hexene
    D) 3–chloro–2,3,5–trimethyl–4–pentene
    E) 3–chloro–1,3,4,4–tetramethyl–1–butene

Answer: A

13) What is the condensed structural formula of the compound propene?
    A) $CH_3-CH_2-CH_3$
    B) $H_3C=CH_2-CH_3$
    C) $H_2C=C=CH_2$
    D) $CH_3-CH=CH_2$
    E) $HC\equiv C-CH_3$

Answer: D

14) What is the condensed structural formula for the compound 3–hexene?
    A)
    $$CH_3-CH_2-CH-CH_2-CH_3$$
    with CH_3 substituent
    B) $CH_2=CH-CH_2-CH_2-CH_2-CH_3$
    C) $CH_3-CH_2-CH=CH-CH_2-CH_3$
    D) $CH_3-CH_2-CH_2-CH=CH-CH_3$
    E) $CH_3-CH=CH-CH_2-CH_2-CH_3$

Answer: C

15) The compound 1–butyne contains
    A) all single bonds.
    B) a double bond.
    C) a triple bond.
    D) a ring structure.
    E) a bromine atom.

Answer: C

16) Some alkenes have geometric (cis–trans) isomers because
    A) the carbon atoms in the double bond cannot rotate.
    B) each of the carbon atoms in the double bond has four different groups attached to it.
    C) one of the carbon atoms in the double bond has two identical groups attached to it.
    D) the carbon atoms in the double bond are free to rotate.
    E) all of the carbon atoms in the compound are rigid and cannot rotate.

Answer: A

17) Which of the following pairs of compounds are cis–trans isomers?
    A)

$$\underset{H}{\overset{CH_3}{>}}C=C\underset{H}{\overset{H}{<}} \quad \text{and} \quad \underset{H}{\overset{H}{>}}C=C\underset{CH_3}{\overset{H}{<}}$$

    B)

$$\underset{CH_3}{\overset{CH_3}{>}}C=C\underset{CH_3}{\overset{CH_3}{<}} \quad \text{and} \quad \underset{H}{\overset{CH_3}{>}}C=C\underset{H}{\overset{CH_3}{<}}$$

    C) $HC\equiv C-CH_3$ and $CH_3-C\equiv CH$
    D)

$$\underset{CH_3}{\overset{CH_3}{>}}C=C\underset{H}{\overset{H}{<}} \quad \text{and} \quad \underset{H}{\overset{H}{>}}C=C\underset{CH_3}{\overset{CH_3}{<}}$$

    E)

$$\underset{H}{\overset{CH_3}{>}}C=C\underset{H}{\overset{CH_3}{<}} \quad \text{and} \quad \underset{H}{\overset{CH_3}{>}}C=C\underset{CH_3}{\overset{H}{<}}$$

Answer: E

123

18) What is the name of the compound shown below?

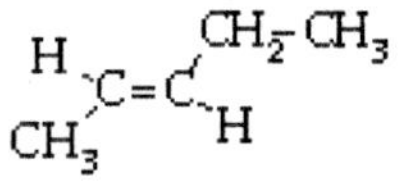

$$\begin{matrix} H & & CH_2\text{-}CH_3 \\ & C=C & \\ CH_3 & & H \end{matrix}$$

    A) 2–pentene
    B) trans–2–pentene
    C) trans–3–pentene
    D) cis–2–pentene
    E) cis–3–pentene

Answer: B

19) The reaction of hydrogen (H_2) and propene using a platinum catalyst is called
    A) combustion.
    B) substitution.
    C) addition.
    D) neutralization.
    E) condensation.

Answer: C

20) The hydrogenation of an alkene gives a(n)
    A) alkane.   B) alkene.   C) alkyne.   D) benzene.   E) isomer.

Answer: A

21) What is the condensed structural formula for the product of the hydrogenation of 2–butene using a platinum catalyst?

    A) $CH_3\text{-}CH = CH\text{-}CH_3$

    B)
$$\begin{matrix} & & Cl \\ & & | \\ CH_3\text{-}CH_2\text{-} & C & H\text{-}CH_3 \end{matrix}$$

    C) $CH_3\text{-}CH_2\text{-}CH_2\text{-}CH_3$

    D)
$$\begin{matrix} & CH_3 \\ & | \\ CH_3\text{-} & C & H\text{-}CH_3 \end{matrix}$$

    E)
$$\begin{matrix} & OH \\ & | \\ CH_3\text{-} & C & H\text{-}CH_3 \end{matrix}$$

Answer: C

22) The reaction of an alkene and water in the presence of an acid catalyst to produce an alcohol is called
    A) hydrolysis.
    B) alkoholysis.
    C) halogenation.
    D) hydration.
    E) hydrohydration.

    Answer: D

23) What is the major product of the reaction shown below?

$$CH_3- CH_2- CH = CH_2 + HOH \rightarrow$$

A)

$$\underset{\underset{CH_3 - CH_2 - CH - CH_2}{|\quad\quad|}}{OH\quad OH}$$

B)

$$\underset{\underset{CH_3 - CH_2 - CH - CH_3}{|}}{OH}$$

C) $CH_3 - CH_2 - CH_2 - CH_2 OH$

D)

$$\underset{\underset{CH_3 - CH - CH - CH_3}{|\quad\quad|}}{OH\quad OH}$$

E)

$$\underset{\underset{CH_3 - CH_2 - C = CH_2}{|}}{OH}$$

    Answer: B

24) Long–chain molecules that consist of many repeating units are called
    A) polymers.
    B) monomers.
    C) organic compounds.
    D) alkenes.
    E) alkanes.

    Answer: A

25) Small molecules that make up the repeat unit in polymers are called
    A) monomers.
    B) alkenes.
    C) alkynes.
    D) minipolymers.
    E) synthetic polymers.

    Answer: A

26) The synthetic polymer polyethylene is unreactive because it is
   A) unsaturated.
   B) a haloalkane.
   C) saturated.
   D) a cycloalkene.
   E) an aromatic compound.

Answer: C

27) What is the starting monomer for the polymer Teflon®?

```
    F   F   F   F
    |   |   |   |
  - C - C - C - C -
    |   |   |   |
    F   F   F   F
```

A)
```
        F
        |
    F - C - F
        |
        F
```

B)
```
        F
        |
    H - C - H
        |
        F
```

C)
```
      F   F
      |   |
    F - C - C - F
      |   |
      F   F
```

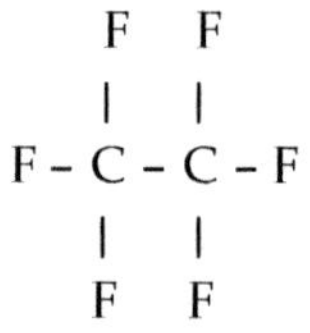

D) C≡F

E) 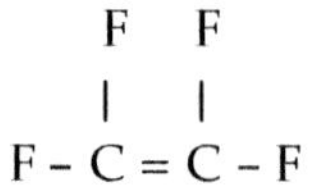
```
      F   F
      |   |
    F - C = C - F
```

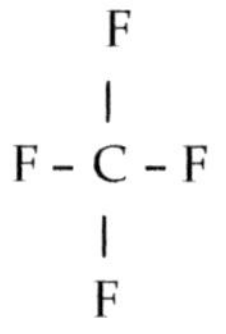

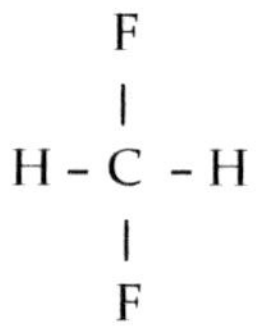

Answer: E

126

28) Which of the following would result from the polymerization of ethene?

A)
$$CH_3 \qquad CH_3$$
$$\mid \qquad\qquad \mid$$
$$-C - CH_2 - C - CH_2 -$$
$$\mid \qquad\qquad \mid$$
$$CH_3 \qquad CH_3$$

B)
$$CH_3 \quad CH_3 \quad CH_3 \quad CH_3$$
$$\mid \qquad \mid \qquad \mid \qquad \mid$$
$$-C - C - C - C-$$
$$\mid \qquad \mid \qquad \mid \qquad \mid$$
$$H \qquad H \qquad H \qquad H$$

C)
$$H \quad H \quad H \quad H$$
$$\mid \quad \mid \quad \mid \quad \mid$$
$$-C = C - C = C -$$

D) $= C = C = C = C =$

E) $- CH_2 - CH_2 - CH_2 - CH_2 -$

Answer: E

29) The structural formula of benzene is often represented as a
   A) ring of five carbon atoms.
   B) ring of six carbon atoms with six double bonds.
   C) ring of six carbon atoms with a circle in the center.
   D) cycloalkane.
   E) cycloalkyne.

Answer: C

30) A compound that contains the ring structure of benzene is called a(n)
   A) alkane.
   B) cycloalkane.
   C) alkyl group.
   D) aromatic compound.
   E) hydrocarbon.

Answer: D

31) The compound below is named

   A) cyclohexane.
   B) cyclohexene.
   C) cyclohexyne.
   D) benzene.
   E) cyclobenzene.

Answer: D

32) What is the molecular formula of benzene?
   A) C_6H_4 B) C_6H_6 C) C_6H_8 D) C_6H_{10} E) C_6H_{12}

Answer: B

33) The odors you associate with lemons, oranges, roses, and lavender are due to
   A) alkenes.   B) alkanes.   C) alkynes.   D) thiols.   E) amines.

Answer: A

34) Insects communicate with chemicals called
   A) markers.
   B) isomers.
   C) signals.
   D) pheromones.
   E) scents.

Answer: D

35) All of the carbon–carbon bonds in benzene are
   A) composed of only two types, single and double.
   B) identical.
   C) double bonds.
   D) single bonds.
   E) circular bonds.

Answer: B

36) Which of the following compounds is an alkene?
   A) $CH_3-CH_2-CH_3$
   B) C_3H_8
   C) $CH_3-CH_2-C\equiv CH$
   D) $H_2C=CH-CH_3$
   E) cyclopentane

Answer: D

37) Which of the compounds is aromatic?

A) CH_2=CH-C=CH_2

B)

C) CH_3-C=CH_2

D)

E)

Answer: E

38) What is the condensed structural formula for the product of the reaction of 2-butene with water and a strong acid catalyst?

A) CH_3-CH=CH-CH_3

B)
$$\begin{array}{c} Cl \\ | \\ CH_3-CH_2-CH-CH_3 \end{array}$$

C) CH_3-CH_2-CH_2-CH_3

D)
$$\begin{array}{c} CH_3 \\ | \\ CH_3-CH-CH_3 \end{array}$$

E)
$$\begin{array}{c} OH \\ | \\ CH_3-CH-CH_2-CH_3 \end{array}$$

Answer: E

39) What is the name of the compound shown below?

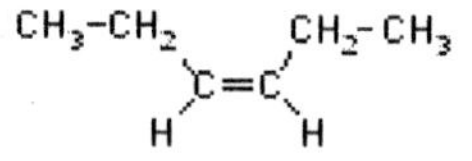

$$CH_3-CH_2 \quad\quad CH_2-CH_3$$
$$C=C$$
$$H \quad\quad\quad H$$

   A) 3-hexene
   B) 3-hexyne
   C) trans-3-hexene
   D) cis-2-hexene
   E) cis-3-hexene
   Answer: E

11.2 True/False Questions

1) Light-induced cis-trans isomerization is an important step in vision.
   Answer: TRUE

2) Propylene is used to induce ripening in fruits.
   Answer: FALSE

3) Fragrances and flavors are often compounds with more than one functional group (for example, an alkene that also contains an aldehyde).
   Answer: TRUE

4) In a cis alkene, the groups are on the same side of the double bond.
   Answer: TRUE

5) In a trans alkene, the groups are on the same side of the double bond.
   Answer: FALSE

6) All alkenes show cis-trans isomerism.
   Answer: FALSE

7) Hydrogenation is used to convert alkenes and alkynes to alkanes.
   Answer: TRUE

8) Hydrogenation of unsaturated vegetable oils raises the melting point and makes them more solid.
   Answer: TRUE

9) Water can be added to alkenes to produce acids.
   Answer: FALSE

10) Polymers are large molecules consisting of repeating units.
   Answer: TRUE

11) Most products made from polymers can be recycled.
   Answer: TRUE

12) One essential building block of aspirin, ibuprofen, and acetaminophen is the benzene ring.
   Answer: TRUE

13) All polycyclic aromatic compounds cause cancer.

   Answer: FALSE

14) The compound is –cis–3–hexene.

   Answer: TRUE

15) The repeating unit in polmers is always ethene.

   Answer: FALSE

11.3 Matching Questions

Match the following organic structures with the appropriate family name.

1)

A) alkane

B) aromatic compound

C) cycloalkene

D) alkene
   aromatic

E) cycloalkane

2) $CH_3CH_2CH_2CH_3$

3)

4)

1) B   2) A   3) E   4) C

131

Match each of the following reactions with its product. Assume any necessary catalysts are present.

5)
$$\begin{array}{l} \quad CH_3 \\ \quad\ | \\ CH_3C = CH_2 + H_2 \xrightarrow{\text{catalyst}} \end{array}$$

6)
$$\begin{array}{l} \qquad CH_3 \\ \qquad\ | \\ CH_3\ C = CH_2 + H_2O \end{array}$$

A)
$$\begin{array}{l} \qquad CH_3 \\ \qquad\ | \\ CH_3\ C\ HCH_2OH \end{array}$$

B)
$$\begin{array}{l} \qquad CH_3 \\ \qquad\ | \\ CH_3\ C\ CH_3 \\ \qquad\ | \\ \qquad OH \end{array}$$

C) $CH_3CH_2CH_2CH_3$

D)
$$\begin{array}{l} \qquad CH_3 \\ \qquad\ | \\ CH_3\ C\ HCH_3 \end{array}$$

5) D 6) B

Choose the type of compound from Column 2 that best matches each item in Column 1.

7) $CH_3-CH=CH-CH_3$

8) CH_4

9)

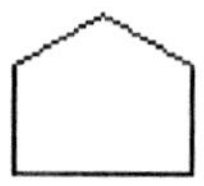

10) $CH_3-CH_2-C\equiv CH$

11)

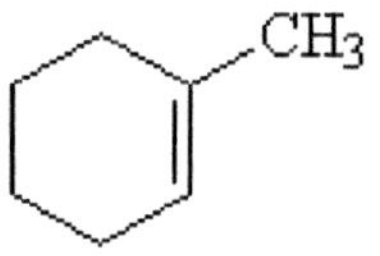

12)
$$\begin{array}{l} CH_3 \\ \ | \\ CH_2 \\ \ | \\ CH_3 \end{array}$$

A) cycloalkene

B) cycloalkane

C) alkene

D) alkane

E) alkyne

7) C   8) D   9) B   10) E   11) A   12) D

Chapter 12 Organic Compounds with Oxygen and Sulfur

12.1 Multiple-Choice Questions

1) Which one of the following compounds is an alcohol?

A)
$$\underset{\underset{\displaystyle CH_3-CH-CH_3}{\vert}}{OH}$$

B)
$$\underset{\underset{\displaystyle CH_3-CH_2-C-H}{\Vert}}{O}$$

C) $CH_3-CH=CH-CH_2-CH_3$

D) $CH_3-CH_2-O-CH_2-CH_3$

E) CH_3-S-H

Answer: A

2) The compound $CH_3CH_2 - SH$ is in the organic family known as
A) ethers.
B) thiols.
C) alcohols.
D) sulfides.
E) amino acids.

Answer: B

3) What is the IUPAC name for this compound?

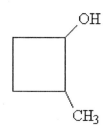

A) methylcyclobutanol.
B) 2-methylcyclobutanol.
C) 2-hydroxy-1-methylcyclobutane.
D) 2-methyl-1-cyclobutanol.
E) cyclobutylmethanol.

Answer: B

134

4) What is the IUPAC name of this compound?

$$\begin{array}{c} \text{OH} \\ | \\ \text{CH}_3 - \text{C} - \text{CH}_3 \\ | \\ \text{CH}_3 \end{array}$$

A) butanol
B) propanol
C) 2-propanol
D) 2-methylbutanol
E) 2-methyl-2-propanol

Answer: E

5) Which of the following compounds is a weak acid?
A) ethanol
B) ethanal
C) phenol
D) cyclohexanol
E) acetone

Answer: C

6) The alcohol in this list that would be most soluble in water is
A) ethanol.
B) 1-octanol.
C) 1-pentanol.
D) 1-hexanol.
E) 1-heptanol.

Answer: A

7) What is the name for this compound?

A) cyclopentanol.
B) cyclohexanol.
C) cyclobenzenol.
D) phenol.
E) glycerol.

Answer: D

8) What is the name of this compound?

$\overset{O-CH_2-CH_3}{\text{[cyclopentane ring]}}$

   A) cyclopentyl ethyl ether.
   B) cyclopentyl ethyl ketone.
   C) 1-cyclopropyl-1-ethylalcohol.
   D) ethylcyclopentanol.
   E) 3-cyclopentylethanol.

Answer: A

9) The common name for the compound $CH_3-CH_2-CH_2-O-CH_2-CH_3$ is
   A) 3-pentanol.
   B) ethyl propyl ether.
   C) 3-hexanol.
   D) 3-ether pentane.
   E) ethyl propyl ketone.

Answer: B

10) The common name of $CH_3-CH_2-O-CH_2-CH_3$ is
   A) dimethyl ether.
   B) diethyl ether.
   C) 2-etherbutane.
   D) butyl ether.
   E) dibutyl ether.

Answer: B

11) The dehydration of an alcohol in the presence of a strong acid yields
   A) an alkane.
   B) an alkene.
   C) a ketone.
   D) an alcohol.
   E) an aldehyde.

Answer: B

12) The dehydration product of $CH_3-CH_2-CH_2-O-H$ in the presence of acid is
   A) $CH_2=C=CH_2$.
   B) cyclopropane.
   C) cyclopropene.
   D) propene.
   E) propyne.

Answer: D

13) When 2-methyl-2-butanol undergoes dehydration in acid, one product is
   A) 2-methyl-2-butene.
   B) 2-methylbutanone.
   C) 2-pentanone.
   D) 2-methylbutanal.
   E) hexene.

Answer: A

14) In the oxidation of an alcohol to a ketone, there is
    A) a loss of hydrogen.
    B) a loss of oxygen.
    C) a loss of carbon.
    D) a gain of hydrogen.
    E) a gain of oxygen.

Answer: A

15) Which of the following compounds is a secondary alcohol?

A) CH$_3$ - CH-O-CH$_3$
         |
        C H$_3$

B) CH$_3$-O-H

C)   OH
                |
    CH$_3$-CH$_2$ -C- CH$_3$
                |
              C H$_3$

D)   CH$_3$
           |
    CH$_3$- C -CH$_3$
           |
          O H

E) CH$_3$ - CH - OH
             |
            C H$_3$

Answer: E

16) In a tertiary alcohol, how many alkyl groups are attached to the carbon atom bonded to the
    –OH group?
    A) none   B) one   C) two   D) three   E) four
Answer: D

137

17) What is the product when this compound undergoes gentle oxidation?

$$CH_3$$
$$|$$
$$CH_3 - C - CH_2 - CH_2 - OH$$
$$|$$
$$CH_3$$

    A) hexanal
    B) 2,2-dimethylbutanal
    C) 2,2-dimethyl-4-butanone
    D) 3,3-dimethyl-1-butanone
    E) 3,3-dimethylbutanal
Answer: E

18) What classification of alcohol undergoes oxidation to yield a ketone?
    A) primary alcohol
    B) both primary and secondary alcohols
    C) secondary alcohol
    D) all classes of alcohols
    E) both secondary and tertiary alcohols
Answer: C

19) Tertiary alcohols cannot be oxidized because
    A) there are no oxygen atoms to remove from the alcohol carbon.
    B) there are no hydrogen atoms attached to the alcohol carbon.
    C) the alcohol carbon is bonded to four groups so no oxygen can be added to it.
    D) the alcohol carbon is bonded to four groups so no hydrogen can be added to it.
    E) the alcohol carbon is too electronegative to have hydrogen removed from it.
Answer: B

20) What classification of alcohol is resistant to oxidation?
    A) primary
    B) secondary
    C) tertiary
    D) quaternary
    E) none
Answer: C

21) Alcohols contain which functional group?
    A) amine   B) amide   C) hydroxyl   D) thiol
Answer: C

22) A primary alcohol has a hydroxyl group bonded to a(n)
    A) singly substituted or unsubstituted carbon.
    B) disubstituted carbon.
    C) trisubstituted carbon.
    D) aromatic carbon.
Answer: A

23) A secondary alcohol has a hydroxyl group bonded to a(n)
   A) singly substituted or unsubstituted carbon.
   B) disubstituted carbon.
   C) trisubstituted carbon.
   D) aromatic carbon.

   Answer: B

24) A tertiary alcohol has a hydroxyl group bonded to at(n)
   A) singly substituted or unsubstituted carbon.
   B) disubstituted carbon.
   C) trisubstituted carbon.
   D) triple-bonded carbon.
   E) double bonded carbon.

   Answer: C

25) A phenol has an –OH group bonded to a(n)
   A) singly substituted or unsubstituted carbon.
   B) disubstituted carbon.
   C) trisubstituted carbon.
   D) aromatic carbon.
   E) tetrasubstituted carbon.

   Answer: D

26) Thiols have structures similar to alcohols except that they contain
   A) three alcohol groups.
   B) more than one carbon.
   C) sulfur in place of oxygen in the functional group.
   D) lithium in place of oxygen in the functional group.
   E) nitrogen in place of oxygen in the functional group.

   Answer: C

27) In the dehydration of an alcohol to an alkene, what is produced in addition to the alkene?
   A) water
   B) hydrogen
   C) oxygen
   D) carbon dioxide
   E) carbon monoxide

   Answer: A

28) When a primary alcohol is completely oxidized, the product is
   A) another alcohol.
   B) a carboxylic acid.
   C) an aldehyde.
   D) an alkane.
   E) a ketone.

   Answer: B

29) Secondary alcohols are oxidized to
    A) carboxylic acids.
    B) ketones.
    C) aldehydes.
    D) esters.
    E) ethers.

Answer: B

30) Tertiary alcohols are oxidized to
    A) secondary alcohols.
    B) ketones.
    C) aldehydes.
    D) carboxylic acids.
    E) none of the above

Answer: E

31) Thiols can be gently oxidized to
    A) disulfides.
    B) aldehydes.
    C) ketones.
    D) carboxylic acids.
    E) thioethers.

Answer: A

32) Thiols are strong-smelling compounds responsible for
    A) fruity odors.
    B) sharp odors.
    C) flowery odors.
    D) skunky or bad smelling odors.
    E) salty odors.

Answer: D

33) What kind of bonds do alcohols form between individual molecules?
    A) oxygen bonds
    B) hydrogen bonds
    C) single bonds
    D) carbon bonds
    E) ionic bonds

Answer: B

34) Which of the following compounds contains a ketone functional group?

A)
$$CH_3$$
$$|$$
$$CH_3-\overset{|}{\underset{|}{C}}-O-H$$
$$CH_3$$

B)
$$\overset{O}{\overset{\|}{CH_3-C-H}}$$

C) $CH_3-CH_2-O-CH_2-CH_3$

D)
$$\overset{O}{\overset{\|}{CH_3-CH_2-C-CH_3}}$$

E) $CH_3 - O - CH_2$
$$|$$
$$CH_3$$

Answer: D

35) Which of the following ketones is the most soluble in water?

A)
$$\overset{O}{\overset{\|}{CH_3-C-CH_3}}$$

B)
$$\overset{O}{\overset{\|}{CH_3-CH-C-CH_3}}$$
$$|$$
$$CH_3$$

C)
$$\overset{O}{\overset{\|}{CH_3-CH_2-C-CH_2-CH_2-CH_3}}$$

D)
$$\overset{O}{\overset{\|}{CH_3-C-CH_2-CH_2-CH_3}}$$

E)
$$\overset{O}{\overset{\|}{CH_3-CH_2-C-CH_2-CH_3}}$$

Answer: A

141

36) What is the IUPAC name for this compound?

$$
\begin{array}{c}
O \\
\parallel \\
CH_3\ C\ H
\end{array}
$$

    A) methyl aldehyde
    B) 1–ethanaldehyde
    C) 1–ethanone
    D) ethanal
    E) methanal

Answer: D

37) Three functional groups found in this compound are

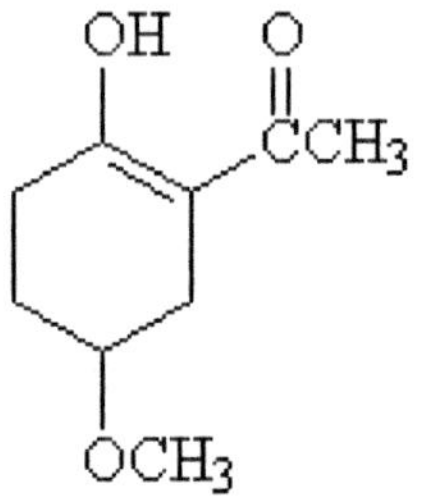

    A) alcohol, aromatic, and ether.
    B) alcohol, aldehyde, and ether.
    C) alcohol, ether, and ketone.
    D) aldehyde, ether, and carboxylic acid.
    E) cycloalkene, alcohol, and carboxylic acid.

Answer: C

38) In all aldehydes except formaldehyde, how many hydrogen atoms is the carbonyl group bonded to?
    A) one   B) two   C) three   D) four

Answer: A

39) How many hydrogen atoms is the carbonyl group in a ketone bonded to?
    A) none   B) one   C) two   D) three   E) four

Answer: A

40) The carbonyl group consists of
    A) a carbon–oxygen–hydrogen structure.
    B) a carbon–oxygen single bond.
    C) a carbon–oxygen double bond.
    D) a carbon–oxygen triple bond.
    E) a carbon–oxygen–carbon structure.

Answer: C

41) In the IUPAC naming system, a ketone is named by replacing the –e in the corresponding alkane name with
   A) yne.   B) ene.   C) al.   D) one.   E) ol.

   Answer: D

42) In the IUPAC naming system, an aldehyde is named by replacing the –e of the name of the corresponding alkane with
   A) yne.   B) ene.   C) al.   D) one.   E) ol.

   Answer: C

43) Formalin is
   A) another name for formaldehyde.
   B) a plastic.
   C) an aqueous solution of formaldehyde.
   D) an excellent solvent.
   E) a polymer.

   Answer: C

44) Acetone is a ketone commonly used as a
   A) preservative.
   B) flavoring agent.
   C) fuel.
   D) solvent.
   E) drain cleaner.

   Answer: D

45) Low-molecular-weight ketones are soluble in water. What is the shortest length of the carbon chain where insolubility becomes important?
   A) one   B) two   C) four   D) five   E) eight

   Answer: D

46) An enantiomer is
   A) a stereoisomer that is not a mirror image of another molecule.
   B) a stereoisomer that is a mirror image of another molecule.
   C) a diastereoisomer.
   D) a constitutional isomer.
   E) a geometric isomer.

   Answer: B

47) Chirality occurs when stereoisomers have mirror images that are
   A) superimposable.
   B) the same.
   C) not superimposable.
   D) not visible to one another.
   E) identical.

   Answer: C

48) How many different substituents are required on a carbon atom for it to be chiral?
   A) one
   B) two
   C) three
   D) four
   E) Any number from 1 to 4; chiralty does not depend on substitution.

   Answer: D

49) Chiral drugs consist of only one enantiomer. The benefits of using a pure enantiomer, rather than a mixture, include
   A) higher potency (lower total dose of drug).
   B) elimination of side effects.
   C) reduced chances of drug interactions.
   D) all of the above
   E) none of the above

   Answer: D

50) Benedict's test requires an aldehyde and an adjacent
   A) saturated carbon.
   B) ketone.
   C) hydroxyol.
   D) phenyl ring.
   E) acid.

   Answer: C

51) The common name for 2-butanone, a readily available solvent, is
   A) methyl acetone.
   B) ethyl methyl ketone.
   C) β-butanone.
   D) butyl ketone.
   E) butyl ether.

   Answer: B

52) Formaldehyde is used industrially to make
   A) polymers.
   B) insulating materials.
   C) carpeting.
   D) all of the above
   E) none of the above

   Answer: D

53) Achiral compounds are those which
   A) have no "handedness."
   B) have different mirror images.
   C) are non-superimposable.
   D) have the same formula but different structures.
   E) are a racemic mixture.

   Answer: A

54) Stereoisomers that are non–superimposable mirror images of each other are known as
   A) enantiomers.
   B) achiral isomers.
   C) superimposable isomers.
   D) anomers.
   E) Fischer projections.

Answer: A

55) Which of the following objects is chiral? Assume that each object has no markings or printing.
   A) an unsharpened pencil
   B) a baseball bat
   C) a glove
   D) a hockey puck
   E) a glass

Answer: C

56) Which of the following compounds is chiral?

A)
```
       H
       |
   H - C - H
       |
       H
```

B)
```
        H
        |
   HO - C - OH
        |
        H
```

C)
```
        CH3
        |
   HO - C - H
        |
        Cl
```

D)
```
       Br
       |
   H - C - OH
       |
       H
```

E)
```
        Cl
        |
   Br - C - Cl
        |
        Br
```

Answer: C

57) An aldehyde forms a carboxylic acid by
    A) oxidation.
    B) reduction.
    C) hydrolysis.
    D) neutralization.
    E) hydrogenation.

Answer: A

58) Which of the following compounds contains an alcohol functional group?

A)
$$CH_3$$
$$|$$
$$CH_3 - C - O - H$$
$$|$$
$$CH_3$$

B)
$$O$$
$$||$$
$$CH_3 - C - H$$

C) $CH_3 - CH_2 - O - CH_2 - CH_3$

D)
$$O$$
$$||$$
$$CH_3 - CH_2 - C - CH_3$$

E) $CH_3 - O - CH_2$
$$|$$
$$CH_3$$

Answer: A

59) Which of the following compounds contains an aldehyde functional group?

A)
$$CH_3$$
$$|$$
$$CH_3- C -O-H$$
$$|$$
$$C H_3$$

B)
$$O$$
$$\|$$
$$CH_3- C -H$$

C) $CH_3-CH_2-O-CH_2-CH_3$

D)
$$O$$
$$\|$$
$$CH_3-CH_2- C -CH_3$$

E) $CH_3 - O - CH_2$
$$|$$
$$C H_3$$

Answer: B

60) Which of the following compounds contains an ether functional group?

A)
$$CH_3$$
$$|$$
$$CH_3- C -O-H$$
$$|$$
$$C H_3$$

B)
$$O$$
$$\|$$
$$CH_3- C -H$$

C) $CH_3-CH_2-O-CH_2-CH_3$

D)
$$O$$
$$\|$$
$$CH_3-CH_2- C -CH_3$$

E) CH_3-O-H

Answer: C

12.2 True/False Questions

1) Alcohols, ethers, and phenols contain oxygen with only single bonds.

Answer: TRUE

2) Alcohols can form hydrogen bonds.
   Answer: TRUE

3) A secondary alcohol can be easily oxidized to a carboxylic acid.
   Answer: FALSE

4) Cycloalkanols are straight chain alcohols.
   Answer: FALSE

5) Derivatives of phenol are often used as antiseptics.
   Answer: TRUE

6) Ethyl ether has been replaced by halogenated anesthetics, which have fewer side effects.
   Answer: TRUE

7) Ethers can only be straight chain compounds.
   Answer: FALSE

8) Alcohols form hydrogen bonds; this accounts for their higher boiling points when compared to similar–sized alkanes.
   Answer: TRUE

9) The oxygen atom in alcohols decreases water solubility of the molecule.
   Answer: FALSE

10) Phenols behave as weak acids in water.
    Answer: TRUE

11) Alcohols can be dehydrated to form alkenes.
    Answer: TRUE

12) Primary alcohols can be oxidized to either aldehydes or ketones.
    Answer: FALSE

13) Secondary alcohols can be oxidized to ketones.
    Answer: TRUE

14) A tertiary alcohol can be easily oxidized to a carboxylic acid.
    Answer: FALSE

15) All aldehydes have a carbonyl carbon bonded to at least two hydrogens.
    Answer: FALSE

16) Many odors from solvents, paint removers, and perfumes are derived from aldehydes or ketones.
    Answer: TRUE

17) In a ketone, the carbonyl group is bonded to two other carbon atoms.
    Answer: TRUE

18) The carbonyl group does not have a dipole.
    Answer: FALSE

19) The suffix *-one* indicates an aldehyde in the IUPAC system of naming.
   Answer: FALSE

20) The suffix *-al* indicates an aldehyde in the IUPAC system of naming.
   Answer: TRUE

21) Acetone is a three-carbon aldehyde.
   Answer: FALSE

22) Acetone is sometimes produced in pathological conditions such as diabetes or when following extreme dieting approaches.
   Answer: TRUE

23) Formaldehyde is used in solution as a germicide and preservative.
   Answer: TRUE

24) Butyraldehyde is partly responsible for the flavor of butter.
   Answer: FALSE

25) The carbonyl group gives aldehydes higher boiling points than alkanes of similar mass.
   Answer: TRUE

26) The carbonyl group gives ketones lower boiling points than alkanes of similar mass.
   Answer: FALSE

27) Carbonyl compounds having fewer than four carbon atoms are very water soluble.
   Answer: TRUE

28) Stereoisomers are not structural isomers.
   Answer: TRUE

29) Enantiomers are mirror images of each other.
   Answer: TRUE

30) A chiral carbon atom can have fewer than four different groups bonded to it.
   Answer: FALSE

31) Enantiomers may have very different tastes or smells.
   Answer: TRUE

32) The biological activity of one enantionmers may be very different from the biological activity of the other enantiomer.
   Answer: TRUE

12.3 Matching Questions

Identify the product, if any, that would form in each of the following reactions.

1) $CH_3-CH_2-CH_2-O-H$

$\xrightarrow{[O]}$

A)

$$\begin{array}{c} O \\ \| \\ CH_3-C-O-H \end{array}$$

2) $CH_3-CH_2-CH-O-H \xrightarrow{[O]}$

    |

    CH_3

B)

$$\begin{array}{c} O \\ \| \\ CH_3-CH_2-C-CH_3 \end{array}$$

3)

$$\begin{array}{c} O \\ \| \\ CH_3-C-H \end{array} \xrightarrow{[O]}$$

C)

$$\begin{array}{c} O \\ \| \\ CH_3-CH_2-C-H \end{array}$$

1) C   2) B   3) A

Match the structural formula with the correct functional group.

4) CH_3-CH_2-O-H

A) ether

B) ketone

5) $CH_3-CH_2-O-CH_3$

C) aldehyde

6) CH_3-CH_2-S-H

D) alcohol

E) thiol

7)

$$\begin{array}{c} O \\ \| \\ CH_3-C-H \end{array}$$

8)

$$\begin{array}{c} O \\ \| \\ CH_3-C-CH_2-CH_3 \end{array}$$

4) D   5) A   6) E   7) C   8) B

Select the correct name for the following.

9) $CH_3-CH_2-O-CH_2-CH_3$

A) diethyl ether

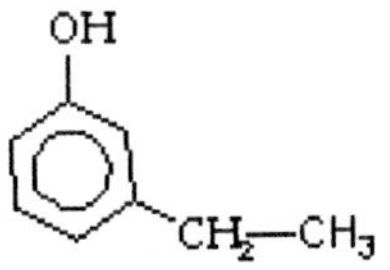

B) diethyl ketone

10)

C) 1-ethyl-3-hydroxycyclohexene

D) 3-propanone

E) propanal

11)   O
        ‖
$CH_3-CH_2-C-CH_2-CH_3$

F) 1-propanone

G) 3-ethylphenol

12)   O
        ‖
CH_3-CH_2-C-H

9) A   10) G   11) B   12) E

Classify the alcohols shown in column 1 as primary, secondary, or tertiary.

13) CH_3-CH_2-O-H A) primary

B) tertiary

14)
$$CH_3-\underset{\underset{CH_3}{|}}{\overset{\overset{CH_3}{|}}{C}}-CH_2-O-H$$

C) secondary

15)
$$CH_3-\underset{}{\overset{\overset{OH}{|}}{C}}H-CH_3$$

16)

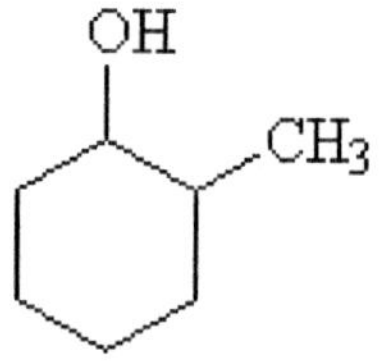

17)
$$CH_3-\underset{\underset{O\,H}{|}}{\overset{\overset{CH_3}{|}}{C}}-CH_2-CH_3$$

13) A   14) A   15) C   16) C   17) B

Identify the family for each of the following compounds.

18) $CH_3-CH_2-O-CH_3$

19)
$$\begin{matrix} & & O \\ & & \parallel \\ CH_3-CH_2- & C & -H \end{matrix}$$

20)
$$\begin{matrix} & & O \\ & & \parallel \\ CH_3-CH_2- & C & -CH_3 \end{matrix}$$

21) CH_3-CH_2-OH

A) alcohol

B) ketone

C) aldehyde

D) ether

18) D   19) C   20) B   21) A

Chapter 13 Carboxylic Acids, Esters, Amines, and Amides

13.1 Multiple-Choice Questions

1) Which functional group is a carboxylic acid?
   A) – OH

   B)   O
        ‖
        – C –OH

   C)   O
        ‖
        – C – O –

   D)   OH
        |
        – C – OH
        |

   E) – CH₂-OH

   Answer: B

2) This functional group is known as a(n)

       O
       ‖
       – C - O –C

   A) ester.
   B) carboxylic acid.
   C) alcohol.
   D) aldehyde.
   E) acetal.
   Answer: A

3) The functional group in acetic acid is called the
   A) hydroxyl group.
   B) aldehyde group.
   C) carbonyl group.
   D) carboxyl group.
   E) ester group.
   Answer: D

4) Which of the following is found in vinegar?
   A) nitric acid
   B) formic acid
   C) acetic acid
   D) propionic acid
   E) butyric acid

   Answer: C

5) The common name of the compound $CH_3CH_2CH_2\overset{\displaystyle O}{\overset{\|}{C}}-OH$ is
   A) acetic acid.
   B) propanoic acid.
   C) propionic acid.
   D) butanoic acid.
   E) butyric acid.

   Answer: E

6) What is the IUPAC name for this compound?

$$CH_3-\overset{\displaystyle CH_3}{\overset{|}{C}}H-CH_2-\overset{\displaystyle O}{\overset{\|}{C}}-OH$$

   A) pentanoic acid
   B) 2-methylbutanoic acid
   C) 3-methylbutanoic acid
   D) 2-methyl butyric acid
   E) 2-methyl-4-butanoic acid

   Answer: C

7) In water solution, how does dilute acetic acid behave?
   A) as a strong acid
   B) as a weak acid
   C) as a strong base
   D) as a weak base
   E) as a neutral compound

   Answer: B

8) Which of the following is the reaction for the ionization of 3–hydroxypropanoic acid in water?

A)

$$\underset{\substack{\displaystyle \| \\ O}}{HO-CH_2-CH_2-C-OH} + H_2O \rightleftharpoons HO-CH_2-CH_2-\underset{\substack{| \\ OH}}{C}-OH + H^+$$

B)

$$\underset{\substack{\| \\ O}}{HO-CH_2-CH_2-C-OH} + H_2O \rightleftharpoons HO-CH_2-CH_2-\underset{\substack{\| \\ O}}{C}-O^- + H_3O^+$$

C)

$$CH_3-\underset{\substack{| \\ OH}}{CH}-\underset{\substack{\| \\ O}}{C}-OH + H_2O \rightleftharpoons CH_3-\underset{\substack{| \\ OH}}{CH}-\underset{\substack{\| \\ O}}{C}-O^- + H_3O^+$$

D)

$$HO-CH_2-CH_2-\underset{\substack{\| \\ O}}{C}-OH + 2\,H_2O \rightleftharpoons {}^-O-CH_2-CH_2-\underset{\substack{\| \\ O}}{C}-O^- + 2\,H_3O^+$$

E)

$$CH_3-\underset{\substack{| \\ OH}}{CH}-\underset{\substack{\| \\ O}}{C}-OH + H_2O \rightleftharpoons CH_3-\underset{\substack{| \\ O^-}}{CH}-\underset{\substack{\| \\ O}}{C}-OH + H_3O^+$$

Answer: B

9) The neutralization of formic acid by NaOH produces
   A) sodium formate as the only product.
   B) formate ion and hydronium ion.
   C) sodium formaldehyde.
   D) methyl alcohol.
   E) sodium formate and H_2O.

Answer: E

10) Which of the following compounds is most soluble in water?
   A) CH_3-CH_2-CH_3

   B) CH_3-CH_2-CH_2-O-CH_3

   C) CH_3-CH_2-CH_2-CH_2-OH

   D)

   $$\underset{\qquad\qquad\qquad\qquad\overset{\|}{O}}{CH_3\text{-}CH_2\text{-}CH_2\text{-}CH_2\text{-}\ C\ \text{-OH}}$$

   E)

   $$\underset{\qquad\ \overset{\|}{O}}{CH_3\ \text{-}C\ \text{-OH}}$$

   Answer: E

11) Which of the following is the reaction for the neutralization of 3–hydroxybutanoic acid with NaOH?

   A)
   $$\underset{\overset{|}{OH}\qquad\quad\overset{\|}{O}}{CH_3\ \text{-}C\ H\text{-}CH_2\ \text{-}C\ \text{-OH}}\ +\ NaOH\ \rightarrow\ \underset{\overset{|}{OH}\qquad\quad\overset{\|}{O}}{CH_3\ \text{-}C\ H\text{-}CH_2\ \text{-}C\ \text{-}O^-\ Na^+}\ +\ H_2O$$

   B)
   $$\underset{\overset{|}{OH}\qquad\quad\overset{\|}{O}}{CH_3\ \text{-}C\ H\text{-}CH_2\ \text{-}C\text{-}\ OH}\ +\ NaOH\ \rightarrow\ CH_3\ \overset{\|}{\underset{\underset{OH}{|}}{-}}C\ \text{-}CH_2\ \overset{\|}{O}\ C\ \text{-OH}\ +\ NaH$$

   $$CH_3\ \text{-}C\ H\text{-}CH_2\ \text{-}C\text{-}\ OH\ +\ NaOH\ \rightarrow\ CH_3\ \text{-}C\ \text{-}CH_2\ \text{-}C\ \text{-OH}\ +\ NaH$$

   C)
   $$\underset{\overset{|}{OH}\quad\overset{\|}{O}}{CH_3\text{-}CH_2\text{-}\ C\ H\text{-}\ C\ \text{-OH}}\ +\ NaOH\ \rightarrow\ \underset{\overset{|}{OH}\quad\overset{\|}{O}}{CH_3\text{-}CH_2\ \text{-}C\ H\ \text{-}C\ \text{-}O^-Na^+}\ +\ H_2O$$

   D)
   $$\underset{\overset{|}{OH}\qquad\quad\overset{\|}{O}}{CH_3\ \text{-}C\ H\text{-}CH_2\ \text{-}C\ \text{-OH}}\ +\ 2\ NaOH\ \rightarrow\ \underset{\overset{|}{O^-Na^+}\qquad\quad\overset{\|}{O}}{CH_3\ \text{-}C\ H\text{-}CH_2\text{-}\ C\ \text{-}O^-Na^+}\ +\ 2\ H_2O$$

   E)
   $$\underset{\underset{OH}{|}\qquad\qquad\overset{\|}{O}}{CH_3\text{-}CH_2\text{-}CH\text{-}\ C\ \text{-}\ OH}\ +2\ NaOH\ \rightarrow\ \underset{\underset{OH}{|}\qquad\qquad\overset{\|}{O}}{CH_3\text{-}CH_2\text{-}CH\text{-}\ C\ \text{-}O^-Na^+}\ +\ H_2O$$

   Answer: A

157

12) Which compound below contains an ester functional group?

A)
$$OH$$
$$|$$
$$CH_3-C\,H-CH_2-CH_3$$

B) $CH_3-CH_2-O-CH_2-CH_3$

C)
$$O$$
$$\|$$
$$H-C-O-CH_2-CH_3$$

D)
$$O$$
$$\|$$
$$CH_3-C-CH_2-CH_3$$

E)
$$O$$
$$\|$$
$$CH_3-C-OH$$

Answer: C

13) Many of the fragrances of flowers and the flavors of fruits are due to
   A) ethers.
   B) carboxylic acids.
   C) esters.
   D) amines.
   E) amides.

Answer: C

14) What is the name of this compound?

$$O$$
$$\|$$
$$CH_3-C-O-CH_2-CH_3$$

   A) ethyl methyl ester
   B) diethyl ester
   C) ethyl methanoate
   D) 2-ether-2-butanone
   E) ethyl acetate

Answer: E

15) The reactants that will form an ester in the presence of an acid catalyst are
   A) two carboxylic acids.
   B) two alcohols.
   C) a carboxylic acid and an alcohol.
   D) an aldehyde and an alcohol.
   E) two aldehydes.

Answer: C

16) Which of these compounds is the ester formed from the reaction of acetic acid and 1–propanol?

A)

$$\underset{\text{CH}_3\text{-CH}_2\text{-}}{}\overset{\overset{\displaystyle O}{\|}}{C}\text{-O-CH}_2\text{-CH}_3$$

CH3-CH2- C -O-CH2-CH3

B)   OH
        |
   CH3- C -OH
        |
        O -CH2-CH2-CH3

C)   OH
           |
   CH3-CH2 -C- OH
           |
           O -CH2-CH3

D)   O
        ||
   CH3 -C -O-CH2-CH2-CH3

E)   O
                      ||
   CH3-CH2-CH2-O-CH2 -C -OH

Answer: D

17) The alcohol and carboxylic acid required to form propyl ethanoate are
    A) methanol and propionic acid.
    B) ethanol and propionic acid.
    C) propanol and propanoic acid.
    D) 1–propanol and ethanoic acid.
    E) 2–propanol and ethanoic acid.

Answer: D

18) The splitting apart of an ester in the presence of a strong acid and water is called
    A) hydrolysis.
    B) saponification.
    C) neutralization.
    D) esterification.
    E) reduction.

Answer: A

19) Which of the following is the reaction for the acid hydrolysis of ethyl formate?

A)

$$\underset{\substack{|| \\ O}}{CH_3 -C -O-CH_3} + NaOH \rightarrow \underset{\substack{|| \\ O}}{CH_3- C -O^-Na^+} + CH_3-OH$$

B)

$$\underset{\substack{|| \\ O}}{CH_3 -C -O-CH_3} + H_2O \rightarrow \underset{\substack{|| \\ O}}{CH_3- C -OH} + CH_3-OH$$

C)

$$\underset{\substack{|| \\ O}}{H- C -O-CH_3} + H_2O \rightarrow \underset{\substack{|| \\ O}}{H- C -OH} + CH_3-OH$$

D)

$$\underset{\substack{|| \\ O}}{H- C -O-CH_2-CH_3} + H_2O \rightarrow \underset{\substack{|| \\ O}}{H- C -OH} + CH_3-CH_2-OH$$

E)

$$\underset{\substack{|| \\ O}}{H- C- O-CH_2-CH_3} + H_2O \rightarrow \underset{\substack{| \\ OH}}{H- C- O-CH_2-CH_3} \\ \underset{OH}{|}$$

Answer: D

20) Which of the following is the reaction for the saponification of methyl acetate?

A)

$$\underset{\substack{|| \\ O}}{CH_3 -C -O-CH_3} + NaOH \rightarrow \underset{\substack{|| \\ O}}{CH_3- C -OH} + CH_3-O^-Na^+$$

B)

$$\underset{\substack{|| \\ O}}{CH_3- C -O-CH_3} + NaOH \rightarrow \underset{\substack{|| \\ O}}{CH_3- C -O^-Na^+} + CH_3-OH$$

C)

$$\underset{\substack{|| \\ O}}{H- C -O-CH_3} + H_2O \rightarrow \underset{\substack{|| \\ O}}{H- C- O^-} + CH_3-OH_2^+$$

D)

$$\underset{\substack{|| \\ O}}{H- C -O-CH_3} + NaOH \rightarrow \underset{\substack{|| \\ O}}{H- C -O^-Na^+} + CH_3-OH$$

E)

$$\underset{\substack{|| \\ O}}{CH_3- C -O-CH_3} + H_2O \rightarrow \underset{\substack{|| \\ O}}{CH_3 -C- O^-} + CH_3-OH_2^+$$

Answer: B

160

21) The reaction of an ester with NaOH is known as
   A) esterification.
   B) neutralization.
   C) saponification.
   D) reduction.
   E) oxidation.

   Answer: C

22) A carboxylic acid is named in the IUPAC system by replacing the –e in the name of the parent alkane with
   A) –oic acid.
   B) –oic.
   C) –carboxylic acid.
   D) acid.
   E) –oate.

   Answer: A

23) When compared to sulfuric acid, how strong are carboxylic acids?
   A) stronger   B) just as strong
   C) weaker   D) not acidic at all

   Answer: C

24) What kind of taste do carboxylic acids have?
   A) sweet   B) sour   C) fruity   D) slippery   E) oily

   Answer: B

25) What is the common name for ethanoic acid?
   A) butyric acid
   B) formic acid
   C) citric acid
   D) stearic acid
   E) acetic acid

   Answer: E

26) What is the irritating acid found in ant and bee stings?
   A) acetic acid
   B) formic acid
   C) citric acid
   D) butyric acid
   E) stearic acid

   Answer: B

27) What therapeutic use is made of α–hydroxy acids?
   A) ulcer treatment
   B) fever reduction
   C) antibiotic
   D) reduction of irregular skin pigmentation
   E) sunscreen

   Answer: D

28) What significant side effect is seen with α–hydroxy acid use?
   A) UV sensitivity
   B) increased thirst
   C) nausea
   D) increased susceptibility to infection
   E) gastric irritation

   Answer: A

29) What α–hydroxy acid is found predominantly in grapes?
   A) tartaric acid
   B) citric acid
   C) lactic acid
   D) glycolic acid
   E) benzoic acid

   Answer: A

30) Which carboxylic acid in the list below is an aromatic carboxylic acid?
   A) acetic acid
   B) benzoic acid
   C) butyric acid
   D) benzene
   E) citric acid

   Answer: B

31) What kind of intermolecular bonding occurs between carboxylic acids?
   A) ionic bonding
   B) nonpolar bonding
   C) covalent bonding
   D) hydrogen bonding
   E) charge–transfer bonding

   Answer: D

32) Why do carboxylic acids have higher boiling points than similar alcohols or aldehydes?
   A) They form dimers that are relatively stable.
   B) They are more water soluble.
   C) They have higher molecular weights.
   D) They have an additional oxygen atom.
   E) The carboxylic acid chain is not linear.

   Answer: A

33) What happens to water solubility as chain length increases in carboxylic acids?
   A) It increases.   B) It decreases.   C) It stays the same.

   Answer: B

34) What is the product of the reaction of an alcohol and a carboxylic acid when reacted together under acidic conditions?
  A) an ether
  B) an ester
  C) a salt
  D) a ketone
  E) an aldehyde

Answer: B

35) Which of these functional groups is likely to give a sour taste to a food?
  A) ester
  B) ether
  C) ketone
  D) carboxylic acid
  E) thiol

Answer: D

36) From what component is the first part of the IUPAC name of an ester (such as methyl anthranilate) derived?
  A) the carboxylic acid
  B) the alcohol
  C) the ether
  D) the ester
  E) the amide

Answer: B

37) What chemical process is responsible for the smell of vinegar in an old bottle of aspirin?
  A) reduction
  B) hydration
  C) hydrolysis
  D) esterification
  E) dissolution

Answer: C

38) What kind of conditions can produce hydrolysis of an ester?
  A) acidic   B) basic
  C) either acidic or basic   D) neither acidic nor basic

Answer: C

39) Which part of a soap is responsible for its ability to dissolve fats and oily dirt?
  A) the hydrophilic end
  B) the hydrophobic end
  C) the carboxylate
  D) the ionized oxygen
  E) the carbonyl group

Answer: B

40) What is the name of the structure formed when a soap coats an oily particle to make it water soluble?
  A) micelle   B) cluster   C) liposome   D) dimer   E) lipid

Answer: A

41) The compound $CH_3-CH_2-NH-CH_3$ is classified as a
   A) primary amine.
   B) secondary amine.
   C) tertiary amine.
   D) quaternary amine.
   E) hydrated amine.

Answer: B

42) Which of the following compounds CANNOT form hydrogen bonds with water?
   A) $CH_3-CH_2-CH_3$

   B) CH_3-CH_2-OH

   C)   O
              ‖
       CH_3- C $-OH$

   D)   O
              ‖
       $CH_3 -C -O-CH_3$

   E) $CH_3-CH_2-NH_2$

Answer: A

43) Aminobenzene is properly known as
   A) toluene.
   B) aniline.
   C) amidine.
   D) histidine.
   E) phenylamine.

Answer: B

44) What is the name of this compound?

       $CH_3-N-CH_2-CH_3$
            |
          C H_3

   A) trimethylamine
   B) diethylamine
   C) ethylmethylamine
   D) ethylmethylnitride
   E) ethyldimethylamine

Answer: E

45) Which of the following represents the complete neutralization of dimethylamine?

A) CH$_3$-NH + H$_2$O → CH$_3$-NH$_2$$^+$ + OH$^-$
    | |
   CH$_3$ CH$_3$

B) CH$_3$-NH + NaOH → CH$_3$-N-Na$^+$ + H$_2$O
    | |
   CH$_3$ CH$_3$

C) CH$_3$-NH + HCl → CH$_3$-NH$_2$ + CH$_3$Cl
    |
   CH$_3$

D) CH$_3$-NH + H$_2$O → CH$_3$-OH + CH$_3$-NH$_2$
    |
   CH$_3$

E) CH$_3$NH + HCl → CH$_3$N$\overset{+}{H}_2$ + Cl$^-$
    | |
   CH$_3$ CH$_3$

Answer: E

46) When ethylamine dissolves in water, a solution of _____ is produced.
   A) ammonia
   B) ethylammonium hydroxide
   C) ethylamine
   D) ethylhydroxide
   E) ethylhydroxylate

Answer: B

47) Diethylamine and HCl react to produce
   A) diethyl chloride.
   B) diethylammonium chloride.
   C) ethylammonium chloride.
   D) ammonium chloride.
   E) butylammonium chloride.

Answer: B

48) The amide formed in the reaction of benzoic acid and ethylamine is
   A)

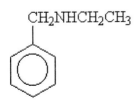

B)

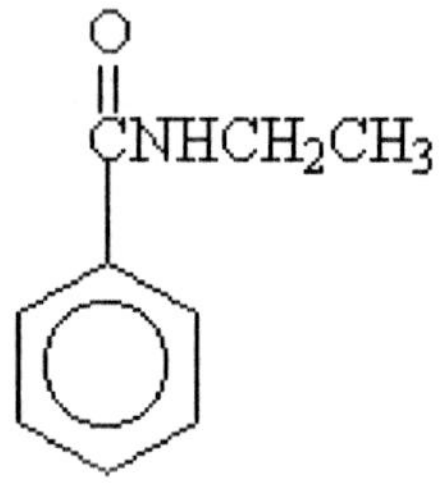

C)

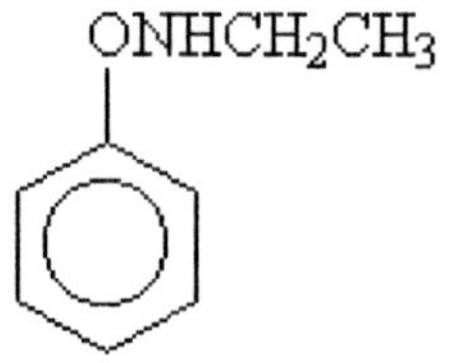

D)

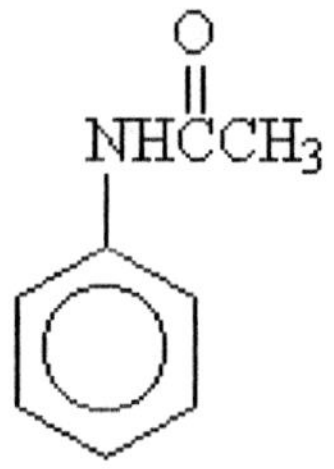

E)

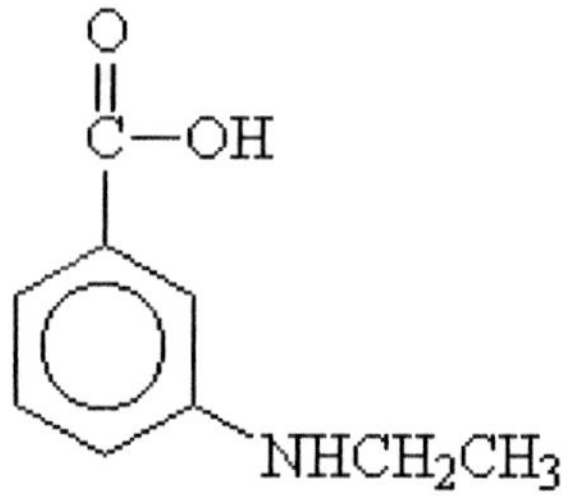

Answer: B

49) When acetic acid reacts with ammonia, NH_3, the reaction yields
    A) acetamine.
    B) ammonium acetate.
    C) ethylammonium hydroxide.
    D) amino acetate.
    E) acetamide.

Answer: E

166

50) Physiologically active nitrogen–containing compounds produced by plants are called
   A) aromatics.
   B) alkaloids.
   C) esters.
   D) polymers.
   E) ethers.

   Answer: B

51) What is the major functional group in the following compound?

$$CH_3-\overset{\overset{O}{\|}}{C}-NH-CH_3$$

   A) ketone
   B) carboxylic acid
   C) ester
   D) amine
   E) amide

   Answer: E

52) With the correct choice of acid, acid hydrolysis of acetamide could produce
   A) acetic acid and ammonium chloride.
   B) acetic acid and methylamine.
   C) ethanol and ammonia.
   D) acetaldehyde and ammonium hydroxide.
   E) formic acid and ethylamine.

   Answer: A

53) Amines contain the element
   A) nitrogen.   B) oxygen.   C) sulfur.   D) astatine.   E) arginine.

   Answer: A

54) In what kind of amine is the nitrogen bonded to two carbon atoms?
   A) primary
   B) secondary
   C) tertiary
   D) quaternary
   E) amide

   Answer: B

55) Which chemical class does phenobarbital belong to?
   A) ester   B) amine   C) amide   D) alkane   E) ether

   Answer: C

56) What functional group is always found in alkaloids (such as caffeine, nicotine, and digitalis)?
   A) amide   B) acid   C) ether   D) amine   E) ester

   Answer: D

57) Aniline is a(n)
    A) primary aromatic amine.
    B) secondary aromatic amine.
    C) heterocyclic amine.
    D) aliphatic amine.
    E) tertiary amine.

Answer: A

58) What prefix is used to show that a small alkyl group is attached to the nitrogen of aniline and not to the aromatic ring?
    A) *N*–
    B) *C*–
    C) Roman numerals
    D) Greek letters
    E) *iso*–

Answer: A

59) How many alkyl substituents does *N*–ethyl–*N*–methylaniline have?
    A) one   B) two   C) three   D) eight   E) none

Answer: B

60) What pharmacologically active amine is responsible for the signs and symptoms encountered in an allergic reaction?
    A) histamine
    B) epinephrine
    C) diphenhydramine
    D) phenylephrine
    E) dopamine

Answer: A

61) A deficiency of which amine is responsible for the signs and symptoms of Parkinson's disease?
    A) histamine
    B) dopamine
    C) epinephrine
    D) diphenhydramine
    E) methedrine

Answer: B

62) The prefix *nor*– in a drug name means that there is
    A) one more amine in the new molecule than in the original.
    B) one more methyl group on the nitrogen atom in the new molecule than in the original.
    C) one less methyl group on the nitrogen atom in the new molecule than in the original.
    D) one less amine in the new molecule than in the original.
    E) one less double bond in the new molecule than in the original.

Answer: C

63) What relation does the boiling point of an amine have to a similar hydrocarbon?
    A) higher   B) lower   C) very similar

Answer: A

64) Amines can form _____ bonds with other molecules.
    A) oxygen   B) hydrogen   C) nonpolar   D) metallic   E) triple
    Answer: B

65) What kind of amine can NOT form hydrogen bonds?
    A) primary
    B) secondary
    C) tertiary
    D) aromatic
    E) substituted
    Answer: C

66) Amines are
    A) Bronsted–Lowry bases.   B) Bronsted–Lowry acids.
    C) neutral in water solution.   D) unreactive.
    Answer: A

67) The odor of an amine can be neutralized with
    A) water.
    B) acids.
    C) bases.
    D) detergents.
    E) solvents.
    Answer: B

68) In what form are amine-containing drugs often administered?
    A) free base
    B) sodium salt
    C) amine salt
    D) water solution
    E) oil solution
    Answer: C

69) What are alkaloids?
    A) physiologically active nitrogen compounds derived from plants
    B) anesthetics found in plants
    C) flavoring agents found in fruits and vegetables
    D) preservatives found in animal tissue
    E) natural steroids
    Answer: A

70) Nicotine, coniine, quinine, atropine, and morphine are all examples of
    A) ethers.
    B) esters.
    C) carboxylic acids.
    D) alkaloids.
    E) amides.
    Answer: D

71) Amides are derivatives of _____ and _____.
   A) amines, esters
   B) amines, acids
   C) alkanes, amines
   D) acids, alcohols
   E) alcohols, acids
   Answer: B

72) What kind of compound is urea?
   A) ester   B) acid   C) amide   D) ketone   E) amine
   Answer: C

73) Amides having fewer than _____ carbons are generally water soluble.
   A) five   B) six   C) ten   D) eleven   E) twelve
   Answer: B

13.2 True–False Questions

1) Soaps are the soluble salt of long chain fatty acids.
   Answer: TRUE

2) Carboxylic acids are strong acids.
   Answer: FALSE

3) Esters are formed from the reaction of an ether with a carboxylic acid.
   Answer: FALSE

4) Carboxylic acids are responsible for the sweet taste of fruits and vegetables.
   Answer: FALSE

5) Aspirin that has a smell of vinegar has broken down by hydrolysis.
   Answer: TRUE

6) The major acidic component of vinegar is formic acid.
   Answer: FALSE

7) It is always safe to use any commercial skin care product without doing a test patch first.
   Answer: FALSE

8) Benzoic acid is an aliphatic carboxylic acid.
   Answer: FALSE

9) Carboxylic acids with more than five carbons are very water soluble.
   Answer: FALSE

10) The boiling points of carboxylic acids are lower than the corresponding alcohols.
   Answer: FALSE

11) Carboxylic acids with four or fewer carbons are very water soluble.
   Answer: TRUE

12) Most of the carboxylic acid in an aqueous solution is ionized.
   Answer: FALSE

13) An ester is derived from an alcohol and a carboxylic acid.
   Answer: TRUE

14) Methyl salicylate (oil of wintergreen) is used therapeutically as a counter-irritant.
   Answer: TRUE

15) Butyl alcohol is one of the reactants used to make methyl butyrate.
   Answer: FALSE

16) Caffeine is an alkaloid.
   Answer: TRUE

17) The amide group is often found in pharmacologically active substances.
   Answer: TRUE

18) The amine function is rarely found in pharmacologically active compounds.
   Answer: FALSE

19) Primary amines contain two carbon-containing groups bonded to the nitrogen atom.
   Answer: FALSE

20) Aniline is the IUPAC approved name for aminobenzene.
   Answer: TRUE

21) The prefix *meth-* means that there is one less methyl group on the nitrogen atom of an amine.
   Answer: FALSE

22) Amines do not form hydrogen bonds.
   Answer: FALSE

23) Tertiary amines form strong hydrogen bonds.
   Answer: FALSE

24) Hydrogen bonds in amines are weaker than those in alcohols.
   Answer: TRUE

25) Amines act as weak acids by accepting protons from water.
   Answer: FALSE

26) Amines are mostly ionized in water.
   Answer: FALSE

27) Amine salts are usually liquid at room temperature.
   Answer: FALSE

28) Amine salts are odorless and usually highly water soluble.
   Answer: TRUE

29) Aniline is an aromatic amine.

Answer: TRUE

30) Crack cocaine is produced by the neutralization and extraction of cocaine from its hydrochloride salt.

Answer: TRUE

31) Quinine is an alkaloid used for treatment of malaria.

Answer: TRUE

32) Atropine and cocaine are used in the diagnosis of eye diseases.

Answer: TRUE

33) Nicotine is a pharmacologically active aromatic amine.

Answer: TRUE

34) Meperidine is a synthetic compound developed from morphine.

Answer: TRUE

35) Lysergic acid is produced by a fungus.

Answer: TRUE

36) Urea is one end product of protein metabolism in humans.

Answer: TRUE

37) Aspartame is a sweetener made from amino acid derivatives.

Answer: TRUE

38) Aspirin substitutes may contain amide rather than ester functional groups.

Answer: TRUE

13.3 Matching Questions

Identify the family for each of the following compounds.

1)
$$CH_3-\overset{\overset{\displaystyle O}{\|}}{C}-CH_3$$

2)
$$CH_3-CH_2-\overset{\overset{\displaystyle O}{\|}}{C}-OH$$

3)
$$CH_3-CH_2-\overset{\overset{\displaystyle O}{\|}}{C}-O-CH_3$$

4) $CH_3-CH_2-NH-CH_3$

5)
$$CH_3-CH_2-\overset{\overset{\displaystyle O}{\|}}{C}-NH-CH_3$$

A) amide

B) carboxylic acid

C) amine·

D) ketone

E) ester

1) D   2) B   3) E   4) C   5) A

Select the correct name for the following.

6)
$$H-\overset{\overset{\displaystyle O}{\|}}{C}-OH$$

7)
$$H-\overset{\overset{\displaystyle O}{\|}}{C}-O-CH_2-CH_3$$

8)
$$H-\overset{\overset{\displaystyle O}{\|}}{C}-O^-Na^+$$

9)
$$CH_3-CH_2-\overset{\overset{\displaystyle CH_3}{|}}{N}-CH_3$$

A) sodium formate

B) formic acid

C) ethyldimethylamine

D) ethyl formate

6) B   7) D   8) A   9) C

Classify the amines shown in column 1 as primary, secondary, or tertiary.

10)   CH₃   A) secondary
              |
     CH₃ –N– CH₃   B) tertiary

                                          C) primary

11) CH₃-CH₂-CH₂-NH₂

12)

13)   H
             |
     CH₃ –N –CH₂-CH₃

14)   CH₃
              |
     CH₃ –C H–CH₂-NH₂

10) B   11) C   12) C   13) A   14) C

Chapter 14 Carbohydrates

14.1 Multiple-Choice Questions

1) A carbohydrate that gives two molecules when it is completely hydrolyzed is known as a
   A) monosaccharide.
   B) disaccharide.
   C) polysaccharide.
   D) starch.
   E) trisaccharide.

   Answer: B

2) Which group of carbohydrates cannot be hydrolyzed to give smaller molecules?
   A) monosaccharides
   B) disaccharides
   C) trisaccharides
   D) oligosaccharides
   E) polysaccharides

   Answer: A

3) A monosaccharide that consists of 5 carbon atoms, one of which is in a ketone group, is classified as a(n)
   A) aldotetrose.
   B) aldopentose.
   C) aldohexose.
   D) ketotetrose.
   E) ketopentose.

   Answer: E

4) A monosaccharide that contains 4 carbon atoms, one of which is in an aldehyde group, is classified as a(n)
   A) aldopentose.
   B) aldohexose.
   C) ketopentose.
   D) aldotetrose.
   E) ketotetrose.

   Answer: D

5) A monosaccharide that contains 6 carbon atoms, one of which is in an aldehyde group, is classified as a(n)
   A) aldopentose.
   B) aldohexose.
   C) ketopentose.
   D) aldotetrose.
   E) ketotetrose.

   Answer: B

6) Ribulose has the following structural formula. To what carbohydrate class does ribulose belong?

$$CH_2-OH$$
$$|$$
$$C=O$$
$$|$$
$$H-C-OH$$
$$|$$
$$H-C-OH$$
$$|$$
$$CH_2-OH$$

A) aldotetrose
B) aldopentose
C) ketotetrose
D) ketopentose
E) ketohexose

Answer: D

7) Which Fischer projection is the mirror image of the structure given below?

$$Br$$
$$|$$
$$HO-Cl$$
$$|$$
$$CH_3$$

A)
$$Br$$
$$|$$
$$HO-CH_3$$
$$|$$
$$Cl$$

B)
$$Br$$
$$|$$
$$Cl-OH$$
$$|$$
$$CH_3$$

C)
$$OH$$
$$|$$
$$CH_3-Cl$$
$$|$$
$$Br$$

176

D)

E)

Answer: B

8) In the L- isomer of a Fischer projection of a monosaccharide, the –OH group furthest from the carbonyl is written
    A) on the left of the top chiral carbon.
    B) on the right of the top chiral carbon.
    C) on the left of the middle chiral carbon.
    D) on the left of the bottom chiral carbon.
    E) on the right of the bottom chiral carbon.

Answer: D

9) One difference between D–glucose and L–glucose is
    A) the open–chain form of L–glucose does not exist.
    B) it is not possible to make L–glucose.
    C) L–glucose has a 5–membered ring , and D–glucose has a 6–membered ring.
    D) only D–glucose can act as a substrate in metabolic reactions.
    E) L–glucose cannot form a closed structure.

Answer: D

10) The sugar also known as grape sugar, dextrose, and blood sugar is
    A) glucose.   B) galactose.   C) fructose.   D) lactose.   E) sucrose.

Answer: A

11) A glycosidic bond between two monosaccharides can also be classified as a(n)
    A) double bond.
    B) ester bond.
    C) ether bond.
    D) achiral bond.
    E) alcohol bond.

Answer: C

12) In a disaccharide, two monosaccharides are joined by what kind of bond?
    A) double
    B) anomeric
    C) alcohol
    D) glycosidic
    E) rotational

Answer: D

13) Which of the following contains a β–1,4–glycosidic bond?
     A) galactose   B) lactose   C) maltose   D) sucrose   E) amylose

    Answer: B

14) Which sugar is NOT a reducing sugar?
     A) glucose   B) fructose   C) galactose   D) maltose   E) sucrose

    Answer: E

Refer to the disaccharide below to answer the following question(s).

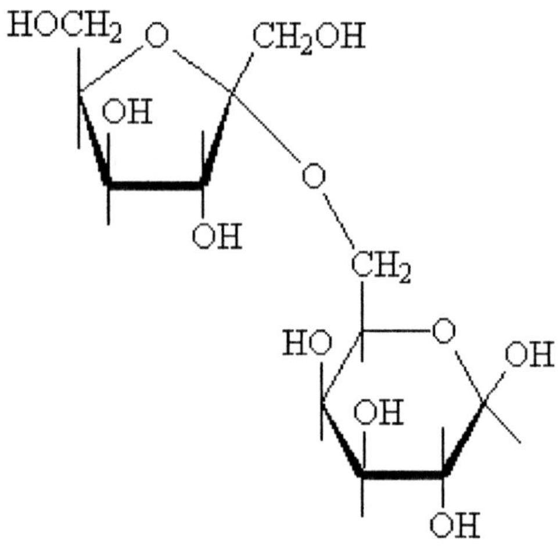

15) In the figure above, the monosaccharide unit on the left is a(n)
    A) aldopentose.
    B) ketopentose.
    C) aldohexose.
    D) aldoheptose.
    E) ketohexose.

    Answer: E

16) In the figure above, the monosaccharide unit on the right is a(n)
    A) aldopentose.
    B) ketopentose.
    C) aldohexose.
    D) aldoheptose.
    E) ketohexose.

    Answer: C

17) Hydrolysis of the disaccharide above gives the monosaccharides
    A) fructose and ribose.
    B) fructose and galactose.
    C) ribose and glucose.
    D) ribose and galactose.
    E) fructose and lactose.

    Answer: B

18) The disaccharide above contains a(n) _____ -glycosidic linkage.
    A) α-1,4   B) β-1,4   C) α-2,4   D) β-2,4   E) α-2,6

    Answer: E

19) Maltose is a
    A) monosaccharide.
    B) disaccharide.
    C) trisaccharide.
    D) polysaccharide.
    E) phosphosaccharide.

    Answer: B

20) Amylose is a
    A) monosaccharide.
    B) disaccharide.
    C) trisaccharide.
    D) polysaccharide.
    E) phosphosaccharide.

    Answer: D

21) Galactose is a
    A) monosaccharide.
    B) disaccharide.
    C) trisaccharide.
    D) polysaccharide.
    E) phosphosaccharide.

    Answer: A

22) Which of the following contains α-1,6-branches?
    A) amylose   B) glycogen   C) cellulose   D) sucrose   E) maltose

    Answer: B

23) Cellulose is not digestible by humans because it contains glucose units linked by
    _____ -glycosidic bonds.
    A) α-1,2   B) α-1,4   C) α-1,6   D) β-1,2   E) β-1,4

    Answer: E

24) Amylose is a form of starch which has
    A) only β-1,4-bonds between glucose units.
    B) only α-1,4-links bonds glucose units.
    C) both α-1,4-and β-1,4-bonds between glucose units.
    D) hemiacetal links joining glucose units.
    E) carbon–carbon bonds joining glucose units.

    Answer: B

25) Amylopectin is a form of starch which has
   A) only β-1,4-bonds between glucose units.
   B) only α-1,4-links bonds glucose units.
   C) both α-1,4-and α-1,6-bonds between glucose units.
   D) hemiacetal links joining glucose units.
   E) carbon–carbon bonds joining glucose units.

Answer: C

26) Cellulose is a polysaccharide which has
   A) only β-1,4-bonds between glucose units.
   B) only α-1,4-links bonds glucose units.
   C) both α-1,4-and α-1,6-bonds between glucose units.
   D) hemiacetal links joining glucose units.
   E) carbon–carbon bonds joining glucose units.

Answer: A

27) Humans cannot digest cellulose because they
   A) lack the necessary enzymes to digest β-glycosides.
   B) are allergic to β-glycosides.
   C) are poisoned by β-glycosides.
   D) have intestinal flora which use up β-glycosides.
   E) cannot digest chlorophyll.

Answer: A

28) Aspartame® and Saccharin® are two examples of
   A) disaccharides.
   B) polysaccharides.
   C) chlorosaccharides.
   D) alcohol sweeteners.
   E) noncarbohydrate sweeteners.

Answer: E

29) Galactose has the structure shown below. It can be classified as a(n)

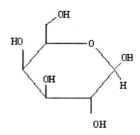

   A) ribose.
   B) ketose.
   C) disaccharide.
   D) monosaccharide.
   E) ketone.

Answer: D

30) Galactosemia is the name of a metabolic disorder. In this disorder, an enzyme is missing that is needed to
    A) make galactose from lactose.
    B) make lactose from galactose.
    C) convert galactose to glycogen.
    D) convert galactose to glucose.
    E) convert α-galactose to β-galactose.

Answer: D

31) Under acid hydrolysis conditions, starch is converted to
    A) glucose.   B) xylose.   C) maltose.   D) galactose.   E) fructose.

Answer: A

32) Maltose can be classified as a(n)
    A) disaccharide.
    B) polysaccharide.
    C) ketose.
    D) pentose.
    E) oligosaccharide.

Answer: A

33) Hyperglycemia is a condition in which
    A) the glucose level in the blood is about 100 mg/dL.
    B) the amount of glucose in the urine is lower than normal.
    C) the glucose level in the blood is higher than normal.
    D) the glucose level in the pancreas is lower than normal.
    E) the glucose level in the liver is lower than normal.

Answer: C

34) Hypoglycemia is a condition in which
    A) the glucose level in the blood is about 100 mg/dL.
    B) the amount of glucose in the urine is higher than normal.
    C) the glucose level in the blood is higher than normal.
    D) the glucose level in the pancreas is higher than normal.
    E) the glucose level in the blood is lower than normal.

Answer: E

35) In the carbon cycle, carbon dioxide and water are converted to glucose and oxygen by
    A) large animals.
    B) insects.
    C) mushrooms.
    D) green plants.
    E) earthworms.

Answer: D

36) The breakdown of glucose to chemical energy for the cells to do work is an example of
    A) oxidation.
    B) respiration.
    C) reduction.
    D) anabolism.
    E) mutarotation.

Answer: A

37) Photosynthesis uses _____ as an energy source.
    A) glucose
    B) carbon dioxide
    C) chlorophyll
    D) oxygen
    E) sunlight

Answer: E

38) Fructose does not undergo hydrolysis because it is a
    A) aldose.
    B) hexose.
    C) reducing sugar.
    D) monosaccharide.
    E) disaccharide.

Answer: D

39) Galactose is a product of enzymatic hydrolysis of
    A) lactose.
    B) glucose.
    C) maltose.
    D) erythrose.
    E) sucrose.

Answer: A

14.2 Short Answer Questions

State whether each of these structures is the α- or β-form.
    1)

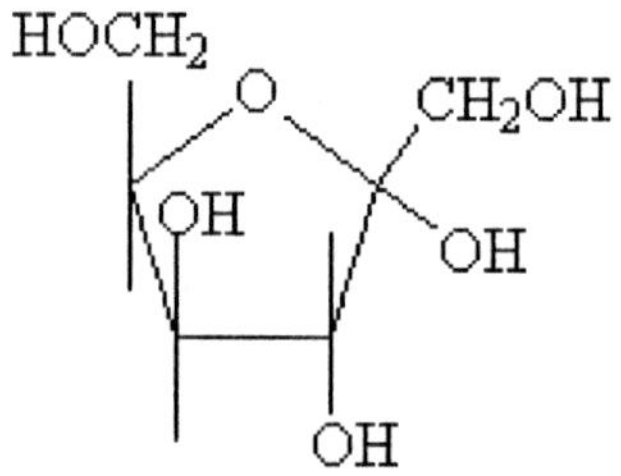

        Answer: α (alpha)

182

2)

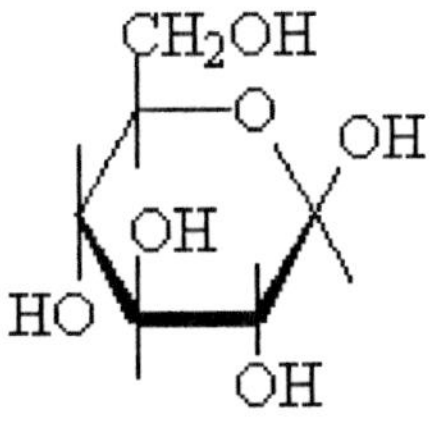

Answer: β (beta)

3)

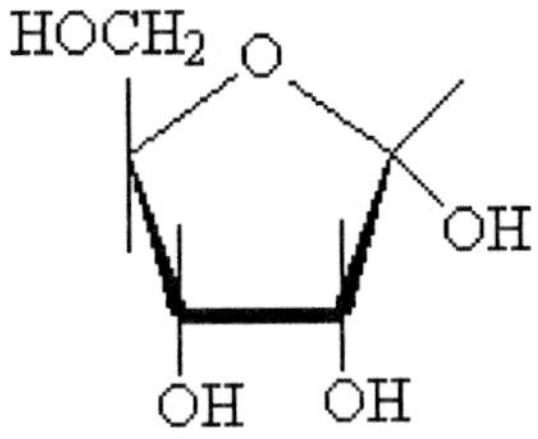

Answer: α (alpha)

4)

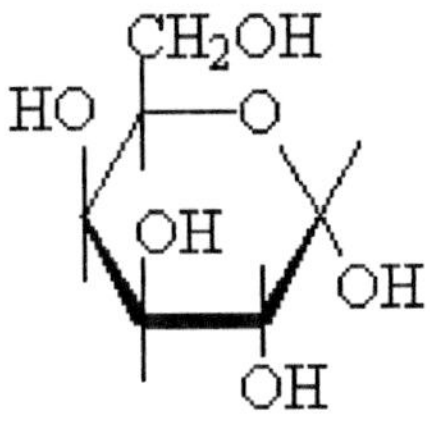

Answer: α (alpha)

5)

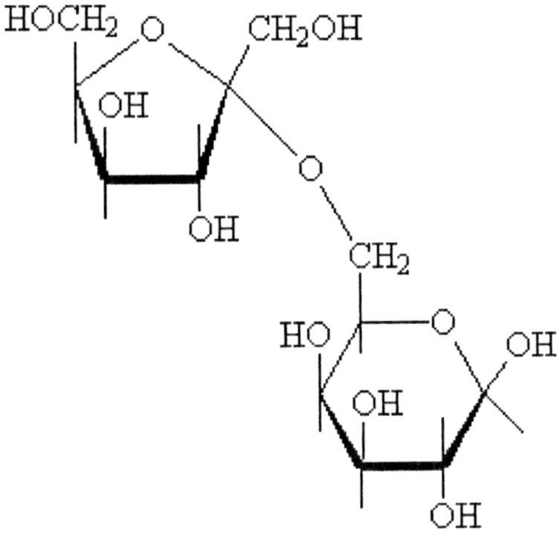

Answer: β (beta)

183

Identify each Fischer projection as the D- or L-isomer.

6)   CHO
             |
        HO — H
             |
         H — OH
             |
           CH_2OH

             -threose

Answer: D

7) CH_2OH
             |
           C = O
             |
        HO — H
             |
           CH_2OH

             -erythulose

Answer: L

8)   CHO
             |
        HO — H
             |
         H — OH
             |
        HO — H
             |
        HO — H
             |
           CH_2OH

             -glucose

Answer: L

9) 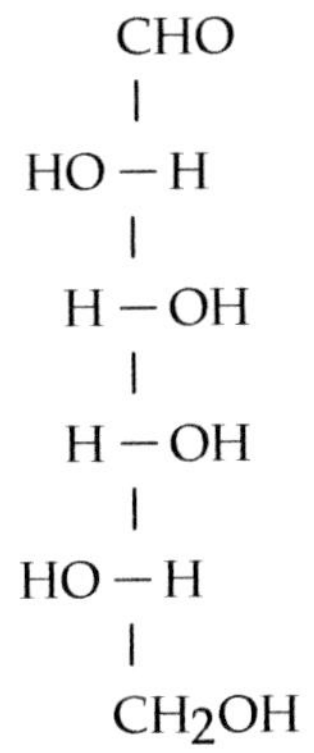   CHO
            |
       HO — H
            |
        H — OH
            |
        H — OH
            |
       HO — H
            |
       CH$_2$OH

        -galactose

   Answer: L

10) 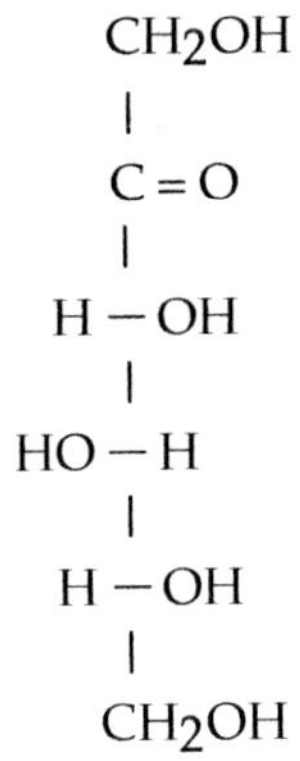   CH$_2$OH
            |
        C = O
            |
        H — OH
            |
       HO — H
            |
        H — OH
            |
       CH$_2$OH

        -sorbose

   Answer: D

14.3 True/False Questions

1) Sucrose is a disaccharide.

   Answer: TRUE

2) A reducing sugar gives a precipitate of silver metal with Benedict's reagent.

   Answer: FALSE

3) Sucrose is made up of glucose units only.

   Answer: FALSE

4) Amylopectin is a straight-chain polysaccharide.

   Answer: FALSE

5) The product of oxidation of an aldose is a carboxylic acid.

   Answer: TRUE

6) The product of reduction of mannose is mannic acid.

   Answer: FALSE

7) Sucrose is a reducing sugar.
   Answer: FALSE

8) The product of reduction of xylose is xylitol.
   Answer: TRUE

14.4 Matching Questions

Select the correct carbohydrate for each description.

1) a carbohydrate that cannot be digested by humans

2) a disaccharide that occurs as a breakdown product of starch

3) a carbohydrate that stores energy in the human body

4) a carbohydrate that is used to build cell walls in plants

5) a monosaccharide that combines with glucose to form lactose

6) a disaccharide found in milk and milk products

7) a disaccharide consisting of glucose and fructose

8) a monosaccharide found in fruit juices and honey, the sweetest carbohydrate

9) an unbranched carbohydrate that stores glucose in plants

10) the product when maltose is hydrolyzed

A) sucrose

B) glycogen

C) galactose

D) maltose

E) glucose

F) cellulose

G) fructose

H) lactose

I) amylose

| 1) F | 2) D | 3) B | 4) F | 5) C | 6) H |
| 7) A | 8) G | 9) I | 10) E | | |

Indicate the monosaccharide(s) produced upon hydrolysis of each carbohydrate.

11) amylopectin

12) lactose

13) glycogen

14) maltose

15) sucrose

A) glucose + galactose

B) glucose + fructose

C) glucose

11) C   12) A   13) C   14) C   15) B

Chapter 15 Lipids

15.1 Multiple-Choice Questions

1) Which statement is NOT true?
    A) Lipids are found in cell membranes.
    B) Lipids are soluble in organic solvents.
    C) There are many different types of lipids.
    D) All lipids contain fatty acids.
    E) Some hormones are lipids.
Answer: D

2) Lipids are compounds that are soluble in
    A) distilled water.
    B) normal saline solution.
    C) glucose solution.
    D) chloroform.
    E) oxygen.
Answer: D

3) Which of the following is NOT a function of lipids in the human body?
    A) energy storage
    B) insulation
    C) protection
    D) emulsification
    E) pH regulation
Answer: E

4) Which of the following lipids will give a single molecule of fatty acid when hydrolyzed?
    A) wax
    B) fat
    C) phospholipid
    D) steroid
    E) petroleum
Answer: A

5) A polyunsaturated fatty acid contains more than one
    A) carboxyl group.
    B) hydroxyl group.
    C) carbonyl group.
    D) long carbon chain.
    E) double bond.
Answer: E

6) Unsaturated fatty acids have lower melting points than saturated fatty acids because
    A) they have fewer hydrogen atoms.
    B) they have more hydrogen atoms.
    C) their molecules fit closely together.
    D) the cis double bonds give them an irregular shape.
    E) the trans double bonds give them an irregular shape.

Answer: D

7) Which of the following is an unsaturated fatty acid?
    A) myristic   B) oleic   C) palmitic   D) stearic   E) lauric

Answer: B

8) Which of the following fatty acids is a solid at room temperature?
    A) palmitoleic
    B) oleic
    C) stearic
    D) linoleic
    E) linolenic

Answer: C

9) Compared to saturated fatty acids, unsaturated fatty acids have
    A) longer carbon chains.
    B) shorter carbon chains.
    C) higher melting points.
    D) lower melting points.
    E) greater intermolecular attraction.

Answer: D

10) Waxes are lipids derived from
    A) a long-chain alcohol and a long-chain fatty acid.
    B) glycerol and three fatty acids.
    C) glycerol, fatty acids, phosphate, and an amino alcohol.
    D) fatty acids, phosphate, and an amino alcohol.
    E) steroids.

Answer: A

11) A triacylglycerol that is solid at room temperature is called a(n)
    A) cephalin.   B) lecithin.   C) oil.   D) wax.   E) fat.

Answer: E

12) Commercially, liquid vegetable oils are converted to solid fats such as margarine by
    A) hydrogenation.
    B) hydrolysis.
    C) hydration.
    D) oxidation.
    E) saponification.

Answer: A

13) Margarine containing partially hydrogenated soybean oil is solid because
  A) it contains only saturated fats.
  B) it contains only trans fatty acids.
  C) some of its double bonds have been converted to single bonds.
  D) it contains only cis double bonds.
  E) it contains only polyunsaturated fatty acids.

Answer: C

14) Palmitic acid is a 16 carbon acid. In a balanced equation, the products of the saponification of tripalmitin (glyceryl tripalmitate) are

A)

$$CH_2-OH \;\; + \; 3\; H_3C-(CH_2)_{14}-\overset{\overset{\displaystyle O}{\|}}{C}-OH$$
$$|$$
$$CH-OH$$
$$|$$
$$CH_2-OH$$

B)

$$CH_2-O^-\,Na^+ \;\; + \; 3\; H_3C-(CH_2)_{14}-\overset{\overset{\displaystyle O}{\|}}{C}-OH$$
$$|$$
$$CH-O^-\,Na^+$$
$$|$$
$$CH_2-O^-\,Na^+$$

C)

$$CH_2-OH \;\; + \; 3\; H_3C-(CH_2)_{14}-\overset{\overset{\displaystyle O}{\|}}{C}-O^-\,Na^+$$
$$|$$
$$CHOH$$
$$|$$
$$CH_2-OH$$

D)

$$CH_2-OH \;\; + \; H_3C-(CH_2)_{14}-\overset{\overset{\displaystyle O}{\|}}{C}-O^-\,Na^+$$
$$|$$
$$3\; CHOH$$
$$|$$
$$CH_2-OH$$

E)

$$CH_2-OH \;\; + \; 2\; H_3C-(CH_2)_{14}-\overset{\overset{\displaystyle O}{\|}}{C}-O^-\,Na^+$$
$$|$$
$$CHOH$$
$$|$$
$$CH_2-OH \;\; + \; H_3C-(CH_2)_{16}-\overset{\overset{\displaystyle O}{\|}}{C}-O^-\,Na^+$$

Answer: C

15) The products of the acid catalyzed hydrolysis of a fat are
   A) the esters of fatty acids.
   B) fatty acids and glycerol.
   C) salts of fatty acids.
   D) salts of fatty acids and glycerol.
   E) phospholipids.

Answer: B

16) A fatty acid salt can act as a soap to remove grease because
   A) the nonpolar tails of the salt dissolve in the grease and the polar salt ends dissolve in water.
   B) the nonpolar tails of the salt cause the salt to float on the surface of the water.
   C) the polar salt ends dissolve in the grease and the nonpolar tails cause the resulting micelles to float on water.
   D) the grease molecules form a thin layer around each salt molecule, making them soluble in water.
   E) the salt molecules combine with grease and either Ca^{2+} or Mg^{2+} to form a precipitate.

Answer: A

17) Glycerophospholipids can interact both with other lipids and water because they contain
   A) double bonds.
   B) polar regions and nonpolar regions.
   C) glycerol.
   D) saturated fatty acids.
   E) cholesterol.

Answer: B

18) The components in the following glycerolphospholipid are

$$CH_2OC(CH_2)_{14}CH_3$$

$$CHOC(CH_2)_{14}CH_3$$

$$CH_2OPOCH_2CH_2NH_3^+$$

   A) sphingosine, palmitic acid, phosphate, and choline.
   B) sphingosine, palmitic acid, phosphate, and serine.
   C) glycerol, palmitic acid, phosphate, and ethanolamine.
   D) glycerol, palmitic acid, phosphate, and galactose.
   E) sphingosine, palmitic acid, phosphate, and ethanolamine.

Answer: C

19) The main lipid components in cellular membranes are
    A) glycerolphospholipids.
    B) fatty acids.
    C) steroids.
    D) triacylglycerols.
    E) waxes.

Answer: A

20) Which of the lipid types listed below is most soluble in water?
    A) triacylglycerols
    B) glycerolphospholipids
    C) oils
    D) steroids
    E) waxes

Answer: B

21) Which of the following compounds is a glycerolphospholipid?
    A) jojoba wax
    B) estrogen
    C) lecithin
    D) triolein
    E) stearic acid

Answer: C

22) Which of the following is a lipid?
    A) cholesterol
    B) nicotine
    C) aniline
    D) lactose
    E) collagen

Answer: A

23) Which of the following is NOT a function of glycerophospholipids?
    A) transport of triacylglycerols
    B) regulation of cellular permeability
    C) protect nerve cells
    D) aid in digestion
    E) transport of cholesterol

Answer: D

24) The most common type of gallstones is composed of almost pure
    A) cholesterol.
    B) waxes.
    C) glycerophospholipids.
    D) calcium salts of fatty acids.
    E) anabolic steroids.

Answer: A

25) Which of the following is NOT a lipoprotein that carries nonpolar lipids through the bloodstream?
   A) glycerol
   B) LDL
   C) HDL
   D) VLDL
   E) chylomicron

Answer: A

26) The steroid hormone that increases the blood glucose and glycogen levels from fatty acids and amino acids is
   A) aldosterone.
   B) progesterone.
   C) cortisone.
   D) estrogen.
   E) prednisone.

Answer: C

27) In the fluid−mosaic model that describes cell membranes,
   A) there are three layers of glycerophospholipid molecules.
   B) two layers of glycerophospholipid molecules have their nonpolar sections oriented to the inside of the membrane.
   C) two layers of glycerophospholipid molecules have their nonpolar sections along the outer surface of the membrane.
   D) A single row of glycerophospholipid molecules forms a barrier between the inside and outside of the cell.
   E) two layers of proteins separate the contents inside a cell from the surrounding fluids.

Answer: B

28) A double cheeseburger with bacon contains 39 g of fat. Calculate the number of kilocalories from fat. (1 gram of fat = 9 kcal).
   A) 4.3 kcal from fat
   B) 39 kcal from fat
   C) 71 kcal from fat
   D) 350 kcal from fat
   E) 640 kcal from fat

Answer: D

For the following question(s), identify the class of lipid to which each of the following molecules belongs.

29)

$$CH_3(CH_2)_{28}\overset{\displaystyle O}{\overset{\displaystyle \|}{C}}O(CH_2)_{19}CH_3$$

   A) wax
   B) triacylglycerol
   C) glycerophospholipid
   D) fatty acid
   E) steroid

Answer: A

30)

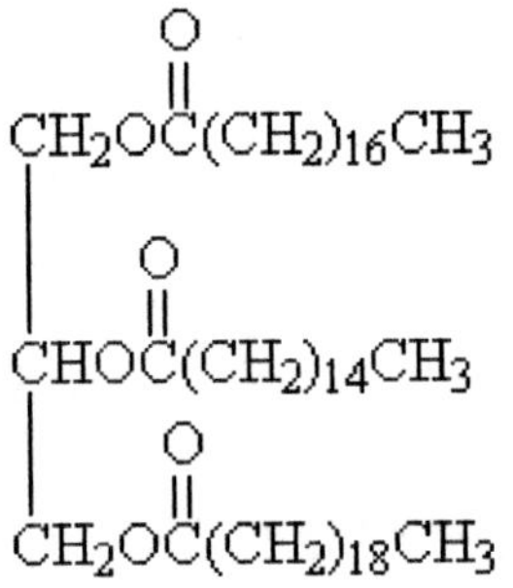

$$\underset{\overset{\|}{O}}{CH_2OC(CH_2)_{16}CH_3}$$

$$\underset{\overset{\|}{O}}{CHOC(CH_2)_{14}CH_3}$$

$$\underset{\overset{\|}{O}}{CH_2OC(CH_2)_{18}CH_3}$$

   A) triacylglycerol
   B) wax
   C) glycerophospholipid
   D) fatty acid
   E) steroid

Answer: A

31)

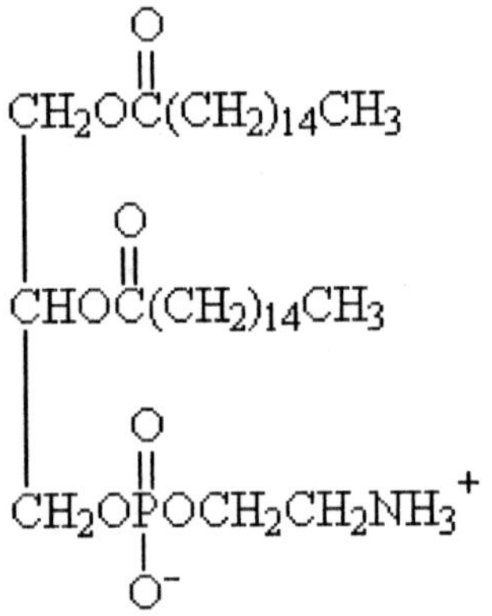

$$\underset{\overset{\|}{O}}{CH_2OC(CH_2)_{14}CH_3}$$

$$\underset{\overset{\|}{O}}{CHOC(CH_2)_{14}CH_3}$$

$$\underset{\underset{O^-}{\overset{\|}{O}}}{CH_2OPOCH_2CH_2NH_3^+}$$

   A) glycerophospholipid
   B) triacylglycerol
   C) fatty acid
   D) steroid
   E) wax

Answer: A

32)

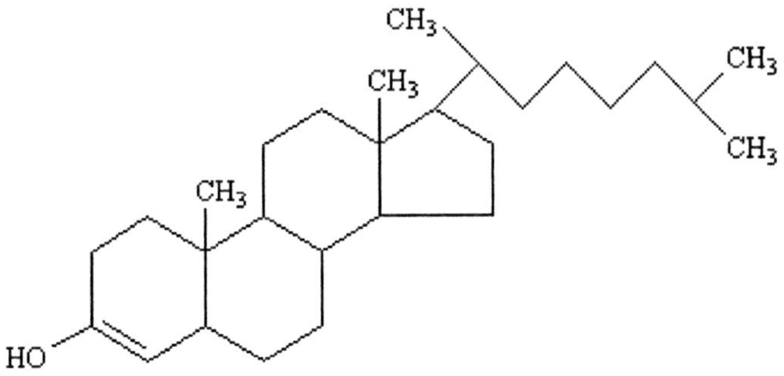

    A) steroid
    B) glycerophospholipid
    C) wax
    D) triacylglycerol
    E) prostaglandin

Answer: A

33) According to the fluid–mosaic model of a cell membrane, the main component of a membrane is
    A) a lipid bilayer.
    B) a membrane protein.
    C) fatty acid.
    D) a steroid.
    E) a prostaglandin.

Answer: A

34) The type of lipid that gives a cell membrane its shape is a
    A) triacylglycerol.
    B) glycerophospholipid.
    C) prostaglandin.
    D) fatty acid.
    E) wax.

Answer: B

35) A lipoprotein particle functions to
    A) dissolve polar lipids for excretion.
    B) metabolize lipids into new substances.
    C) dissolve polar lipids in urine.
    D) transport nonpolar lipid to body cells.
    E) store lipids in the tissues.

Answer: D

36) Synthesis of cholesterol takes place in the
    A) liver.
    B) gall bladder.
    C) small intestine.
    D) large intestine.
    E) pancreas.

Answer: A

Answer the following question(s) about the diagram shown below.

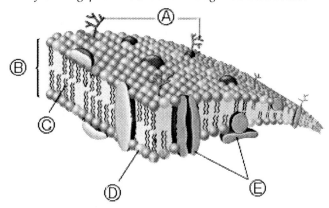

37) In this diagram of a cell membrane, the small branched object labeled (A) is part of a
    A) steroid.
    B) hydrophobic region.
    C) membrane protein.
    D) glycerophospholipid.
    E) carbohydrate side chain.

   Answer: E

38) In this diagram of a cell membrane, the objects labeled (E) are
    A) steroids.
    B) hydrophobic regions.
    C) proteins.
    D) phospholipids.
    E) carbohydrate side chains.

   Answer: C

39) In this diagram of a cell membrane, the object labeled (C) is a
    A) steroid.
    B) protein
    C) phospholipid.
    D) mitochondrion.
    E) carbohydrate side chain.

   Answer: C

40) In this diagram of a cell membrane, the object labeled (B) is a
    A) steroid.
    B) hydrophobic region.
    C) membrane protein.
    D) glycerophospholipid bilayer.
    E) carbohydrate side chain.

   Answer: D

15.2 Bimodal Questions

1) Cholesterol belongs to the _____ group of lipids.
   A) phospholipid
   B) steroid
   C) prostaglandin
   D) triacylglycerol
   E) wax

   Answer: B

2) A precursor of prostaglandins is _____ acid.
   A) oleic
   B) linoleic
   C) arachidonic
   D) tauric
   E) palmitic

   Answer: C

3) In a simple model of atherosclerosis and heart disease, the compound that forms plaques that adhere to the walls of the blood vessels is _____.
   A) cholesterol
   B) carnauba wax
   C) stearic acid
   D) glycerol
   E) oleic acid

   Answer: A

4) The name of the reaction that occurs when a fat reacts with sodium hydroxide and water is
   _____.
   A) hydrogenation
   B) reduction
   C) hydration
   D) oxidation
   E) saponification

   Answer: E

15.3 True/False Questions

1) The catalyst needed for saponification is H^+ ion.
   Answer: FALSE

2) Olestra is a triacylglycerol.
   Answer: FALSE

3) Hydrogenation of a double bond in a triacylglycerol requires a catalyst.
   Answer: TRUE

4) Most plant lipids are saturated lipids.
   Answer: FALSE

5) The head of a triacylglycerol is the polar end of the molecule.

Answer: TRUE

6) The tail of a triacylglycerol is the nonpolar end.

Answer: TRUE

7) One function of phospholipids is to provide structure to cell membranes.

Answer: TRUE

8) In the fluid–mosaic model of cell membranes, the lipid molecules are oriented with their heads to the outside of the membrane.

Answer: TRUE

9) Glycoproteins are components of cell membranes.

Answer: TRUE

10) The interior of a lipid bilayer is the hydrophilic region.

Answer: FALSE

11) Waxes do not contain fatty acids.

Answer: FALSE

12) Steroids do not contain fatty acids.

Answer: TRUE

15.4 Matching Questions

Match the following.

1) Triacylglycerols are formed from glycerol and _____.

2) a lipid that cannot be hydrolyzed

3) the functional group of triacylglycerols

4) a fatty acid with at least one double bond

5) the process of converting unsaturated fats into saturated fats

6) the melting points of saturated fats compared to unsaturated fats

7) a source of most saturated fats

8) a characteristic common to most lipids

9) the product of reacting a triacylglycerol with a strong base and water

A) soap

B) cholesterol

C) glycerin

D) animals

E) hydrolysis

F) lower

G) ester

H) insoluble in water

I) plants

J) higher

K) fatty acids

L) unsaturated

M) hydrogenation

1) K	2) B	3) G	4) L	5) M	6) J
7) D	8) H	9) A			

Select the type of lipid that matches the description.

10) triolein

11) aldosterone

12) testosterone

13) cephalin

14) oleic acid

A) glycerophospholipid

B) steroid

C) fatty acid

D) triacylglycerol

10) D	11) B	12) B	13) A	14) C

199

Chapter 16   Amino Acids, Proteins, and Enzymes

16.1 Multiple-Choice Questions

1) Which of the following is NOT a function of proteins?
   A) provide structural components
   B) stores the genetic information of a living organism
   C) movement of muscles
   D) catalyze reactions in the cells
   E) transport substances through the bloodstream
   Answer: B

2) Collagen, a protein found in tendons and cartilage, would be classified as a _____ protein.
   A) catalytic   B) structural   C) transport   D) storage   E) hormone
   Answer: B

3) Sucrase, the protein that facilitates the hydrolysis of sucrose, would be classified as a _____ protein.
   A) transport
   B) hormonal
   C) catalytic
   D) structural
   E) contractile
   Answer: C

4) The structural formulas of amino acids are the same EXCEPT for the
   A) carboxyl group.
   B) alpha carbon.
   C) amino group.
   D) side (R) group.
   E) hydrogen bonding.
   Answer: D

5) The following amino acid side chain is

   $- C H-CH_3$
   |
   CH_3

   A) polar.
   B) hydrophobic.
   C) hydrophilic.
   D) acidic.
   E) basic.
   Answer: B

6) Which of the following would be most likely to be deficient in at least one essential amino acid?
   A) eggs   B) milk   C) beans   D) steak   E) ham
   Answer: C

7) Amino acids that are not synthesized in the body and must be obtained from the diet are called
    A) essential.
    B) polar.
    C) nonpolar.
    D) complete.
    E) incomplete.

Answer: A

8) The R group for serine is $-CH_2-OH$. As a zwitterion, serine has the structural formula

A) CH_2-OH
              |
      $NH_2-CH-COOH$

B) CH_2-OH
              |
      $NH_2-CH-COO^-$

C) CH_2-O^-
        + |
      $NH_3-CH-COOH$

D) CH_2-OH
        + |
      $NH_3-CH-COOH$

E) CH_2-OH
        + |
      $NH_3-CH-COO^-$

Answer: E

9) Which of the following functional groups of an amino acid would be in the ionized state at high pH?

A) O
||
-C-OH

B) $-CH_2-OH$

C) $-CH_3$

D) O
||
$-CNH_2$

E)

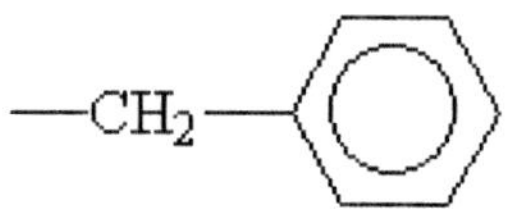

Answer: A

10) Which of the following is the correct structure for Ser–Ala–Asp? The appropriate side chains look like this.

Ala: $-CH_3$; Ser: $-CH_2-OH$; Asp: $-CH_2-C(=O)-OH$

A)

```
                    OH              COOH
                    |               |
     CH3  O         CH2  O          CH2  O
     |    ||        |    ||         |    ||
H3N - CH - C - NH - CH - C - NH - CH - CO-
```

B)

```
     COOH                           OH
     |                              |
     CH2  O         CH3  O          CH2  O
     |    ||        |    ||         |    ||
H3N - CH - C - NH - CH - C - NH - CH - CO-
```

C)

```
     OH             COOH
     |              |
     CH2  O         CH2  O          CH3  O
     |    ||        |    ||         |    ||
H3N - CH - C - NH - CH - C - NH - CH - CO-
```

D)

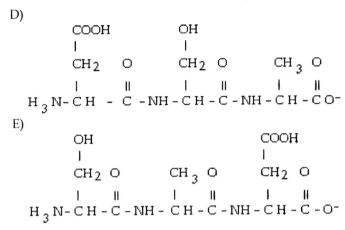

E)

$$H_3N-CH-C-NH-CH-C-NH-CH-C-O^-$$

Answer: E

11) The peptide bonds that link amino acids in a protein are
   A) ester bonds.
   B) ether bonds.
   C) amide bonds.
   D) glycosidic bonds.
   E) sulfide bonds.

Answer: C

12) The bonds that are important in the secondary structure of a protein are
   A) hydrogen bonds.
   B) hydrophobic interactions.
   C) disulfide bonds.
   D) salt bridges.
   E) peptide bonds.

Answer: A

13) Which of the following is a secondary protein structure?
   A) α–helix
   B) Ser–Met–Ala–Gly–Ile
   C) disulfide bond
   D) salt bridges
   E) hydrophobic interactions

Answer: A

14) Which R group would most likely be found in a hydrophobic area of the tertiary structure of a globular protein?

A) $-CH_2-OH$

B) $-CH_2-COO^-$

C)

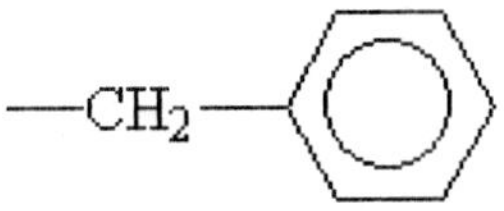

$$-CH_2-\bigcirc$$

D) $-CH_2-CH_2-CH_2-CH_2-\overset{+}{N}H_3$

E)

$$-CH_2-\overset{\overset{\textstyle O}{\|}}{C}-NH_2$$

Answer: C

15) What type of interaction would you expect between the following R groups in the tertiary structure of a protein?

$$-CH_2-\overset{\overset{\textstyle O}{\|}}{C}O^- \quad \text{and} \quad -CH_2-CH_2-CH_2-CH_2-NH_3^+$$

A) disulfide bonds
B) salt bridges
C) hydrogen bonds
D) hydrophobic interactions
E) peptide bonds

Answer: B

16) What kinds of interactions are NOT part of tertiary protein structure?

A) peptide bonds
B) disulfide bonds
C) hydrophilic interactions
D) salt bridges
E) hydrophobic interactions

Answer: A

17) Acids and bases denature a protein by disrupting

A) peptide bonds and salt bridges.
B) amide bonds and alkene bonds.
C) hydrophobic interactions and peptide bonds.
D) salt bridges and hydrophobic interactions.
E) salt bridges and hydrogen bonds.

Answer: E

18) Heat denatures a protein by disrupting
    A) salt bridges and peptide bonds.
    B) hydrophobic bonds and hydrogen bonds.
    C) peptide bonds and hydrophobic bonds.
    D) disulfide bonds and peptide bonds.
    E) hydrogen bonds and disulfide bonds.

Answer: B

19) The secondary structure of collagen is distinguished by
    A) single α-helix strands.
    B) double α-helix strands.
    C) many α-helixes wound into fibrils.
    D) a braided triple helix.
    E) many glycoside links.

Answer: D

20) The fibrous protein responsible for the structure of hair and wool is
    A) keratin.
    B) collagen.
    C) endorphin.
    D) myosin.
    E) casein.

Answer: A

21) In the peptide Ala–Try–Gly–Phe, the N–terminal amino acid is
    A) alanine.
    B) phenylalanine.
    C) tryptophan.
    D) aspartic acid.
    E) glycine.

Answer: A

22) In the peptide Ser–Cys–Ala–Gly, the C–terminal end is
    A) serine.
    B) serotonin.
    C) glycine.
    D) glycerine.
    E) alanine.

Answer: C

23) A chain made of more than 50 amino acids is usually referred to as a(n)
    A) peptide.   B) protein.   C) enzyme.   D) globulin.   E) hormone.

Answer: B

24) The α-helix of the secondary structure of a protein is held together by _____ between two widely separated parts of a protein chain.
   A) hydrogen bonds
   B) disulfide bridges
   C) salt bridges
   D) hydrophilic interactions
   E) hydrophobic interactions

Answer: A

25) In the β-pleated sheet secondary structure of a protein, two or more amino acid sequences in separate parts of the protein are held together
   A) in a coil, by hydrogen bonding.
   B) in random order, due to hydrophobic interactions.
   C) in a triple helix.
   D) in a double helix.
   E) in a zig-zag conformation, by hydrogen bonding.

Answer: E

26) Enkephalins are polypeptides that have
   A) a sweet taste.
   B) a bitter taste.
   C) extra caloric value.
   D) pain-killing properties.
   E) hormone activity.

Answer: D

27) A completely vegetarian diet will contain all the essential amino acids if it includes
   A) wheat and rice.
   B) rice and beans.
   C) almonds and walnuts.
   D) corn and beans.
   E) wheat and corn.

Answer: B

28) In insulin, two peptide chains are held together in a single unit by
   A) disulfide bridges.
   B) hydrogen bonds.
   C) salt bridges.
   D) a prosthetic group.
   E) a β-pleated sheet.

Answer: A

29) Hemoglobin is an example of a protein with
   A) primary structure only.
   B) two protein chains held together.
   C) a globular structure.
   D) primarily a β-pleated sheet structure.
   E) primarily an α-helix structure.

Answer: C

30) The heme in hemoglobin is a(n)
    A) protein chain.
    B) small molecule within a protein.
    C) helix area in the hemoglobin molecule.
    D) pleated sheet area in the hemoglobin molecule.
    E) oxygen molecule within the hemoglobin molecule.

Answer: B

31) Within hemoglobin, the heme functions as
    A) a disulfide bridge.
    B) an oxygen carrier.
    C) a reducing agent.
    D) an α subunit.
    E) one of the four protein subunits.

Answer: B

32) Hemoglobin has a total of _____ protein chains in its quaternary structure.
    A) one   B) two   C) three   D) four   E) five

Answer: D

33) Wool is primarily made up of
    A) protein.
    B) carbohydrate.
    C) globin.
    D) triacylglycerols.
    E) enkephalin.

Answer: A

34) The function of myoglobin is to
    A) carry vitamins in the blood.
    B) carry oxygen in the blood.
    C) support the skeletal muscles.
    D) carry oxygen in the muscle.
    E) provide strength in cartilage.

Answer: D

35) In sickle-cell anemia, the hemoglobin molecules
    A) come apart into separate chains.
    B) enlarge to twice normal size.
    C) clump together into insoluble fibers.
    D) dissolve in the plasma.
    E) undergo crenation.

Answer: C

36) Denaturation of a protein
    A) changes the primary structure of a protein.
    B) disrupts the secondary, tertiary, or quaternary structure of a protein.
    C) is always irreversible.
    D) hydrolyzes peptide bonds.
    E) can only occur in a protein with quaternary structure.

Answer: B

37) One heavy metal that can cause denaturation of a protein is
    A) silver.   B) sodium.   C) barium.   D) iron.   E) calcium.

    Answer: A

38) Heavy metals denature proteins by
    A) releasing amino acids.
    B) disrupting hydrophobic interactions.
    C) changing the pH of the protein solution.
    D) changing the temperature of the protein solution.
    E) disrupting disulfide bonds.

    Answer: E

39) An acid can denature a protein by
    A) agitating the protein chains.
    B) disrupting hydrogen bonds between side chains.
    C) disrupting hydrophobic interactions within a protein chain.
    D) removing helping molecules such as heme.
    E) breaking disulfide bridges.

    Answer: B

40) Glycine is the only naturally occurring amino acid that is
    A) negatively charged.
    B) positively charged.
    C) neutral.
    D) in the L– form.
    E) achiral.

    Answer: E

41) In a typical amino acid zwitterion, the carboxylic acid end is
    A) positively charged.
    B) negatively charged.
    C) neutral.
    D) soluble in a nonpolar solvent.
    E) attached to an amine.

    Answer: B

42) Methionine is an amino acid that contains
    A) a sulfur atom.
    B) a chlorine atom.
    C) a sodium atom.
    D) a phenyl ring.
    E) a heterocyclic ring.

    Answer: A

43) Disulfide bonds in a protein chain connect
    A) an amine and a carboxylic acid group.
    B) an alcohol and a carboxylic acid group.
    C) tryptophan and alanine residues.
    D) two cysteine residues.
    E) two asparagine residues.

    Answer: D

44) The side chain for histidine is classified as a _____ side chain.
    A) basic   B) neutral   C) acidic   D) nonpolar   E) polar

    Answer: A

45) At a pH > 9, the zwitterion of glycine will have
    A) a net positive charge.
    B) a net negative charge.
    C) an overall charge of zero.
    D) low solubility in water.
    E) a negative charge on the nitrogen.

    Answer: B

46) At a pH < 5, the zwitterion for alanine (pI = 6) will have
    A) a net positive charge.
    B) a net negative charge.
    C) an overall charge of zero.
    D) low solubility in water.
    E) a negative charge on the carboxyl group.

    Answer: A

47) What is the structural formula of glutamic acid (pl = 3.2) at pH = 1?

A)

$$NH_2$$
$$|$$
$$H - C - CH_2-CH_2 - COOH$$
$$|$$
$$COOH$$

B)

$$NH_2$$
$$|$$
$$H - C - CH_2-CH_2 - COOH$$
$$|$$
$$COO^-$$

C)

$$NH_2$$
$$|$$
$$H - C - CH_2-CH_2 - COO^-$$
$$|$$
$$COO^-$$

D)

$$NH_3^+$$
$$|$$
$$H - C - CH_2-CH_2 - COO^-$$
$$|$$
$$COO^-$$

E)

$$NH_3^+$$
$$|$$
$$H - C - CH_2-CH_2 - COOH$$
$$|$$
$$COOH$$

Answer: E

48) A basic amino acid has a side chain that contains
  A) an amine group.
  B) a carboxyl group.
  C) a methyl group.
  D) an alcohol group.
  E) a thiol group.

Answer: A

49) Enkephalins, naturally produced opiates in the body, are found in
  A) muscles and bone tissue.
  B) brain and kidney tissue.
  C) thalamus and spinal cord tissue.
  D) heart and lung tissue.
  E) pancreas and liver tissue.

Answer: C

50) To what main class of enzymes does the enzyme that catalyzes the conversion of lactose to galactose and glucose belong?
   A) oxidoreductase
   B) transferase
   C) hydrolase
   D) lyase
   E) isomerase

Answer: C

51) To what main class of enzymes does the enzyme that catalyzes the following reaction belong?

$$CH_3 -\overset{\overset{\textstyle O}{\|}}{C} -COO^- \;\rightarrow\; CH_3 -\overset{\overset{\textstyle OH}{|}}{C}H-COO^-$$

   A) oxidoreductase
   B) transferase
   C) hydrolase
   D) lyase
   E) isomerase

Answer: A

52) To what main class of enzymes does the enzyme that catalyzes the following reaction belong?

   ser-ala → ser + ala

   A) oxidoreductase
   B) transferase
   C) hydrolase
   D) lyase
   E) isomerase

Answer: C

53) Compared to an uncatalyzed reaction, an enzyme-catalyzed reaction
   A) uses less substrate.
   B) produces different products.
   C) occurs at a faster rate.
   D) requires more energy.
   E) requires a higher temperature.

Answer: C

54) The formation of an enzyme-substrate complex is the _____ step in enzyme action.
   A) first   B) second   C) third   D) fourth   E) last

Answer: A

55) The active site of an enzyme
   A) is remote from the site of substrate attachment.
   B) is converted to a product.
   C) catalyzes the reaction.
   D) increases the energy of reaction.
   E) includes the entire enzyme.

Answer: C

56) The water-soluble B and C vitamins supply
   A) essential amino acids.
   B) substrates necessary for most of the reactions in the body.
   C) essential fatty acids.
   D) coenzymes required by some enzymes.
   E) competitive inhibitors needed to regulate enzyme activity.

Answer: D

57) The optimum temperature for sucrase activity is 37 °C. The hydrolysis of sucrose is slowest at which temperature in the choices below?
   A) 0 °C   B) 10 °C   C) 20 °C   D) 25 °C   E) 45 °C

Answer: A

58) Which of the following is NOT true for a competitive inhibitor?
   A) It occupies the active site.
   B) It cannot be converted to products.
   C) It has a structure similar to the substrate.
   D) Increasing the substrate concentration can reverse competitive inhibition.
   E) It binds to the enzyme at a site remote from the active site.

Answer: E

59) A noncompetitive inhibitor
   A) binds at the active site of the enzyme.
   B) alters the three-dimensional structure of the enzyme.
   C) increases the rate of the enzyme-catalyzed reaction.
   D) has a structure similar to the substrate.
   E) has its effect reversed by adding more substrate.

Answer: B

60) The purpose of the many chemical reactions in our bodies is to
   A) store chemical energy in the body for future use.
   B) produce the essential amino acids.
   C) produce the essential lipids.
   D) release chemical energy for the production of macromolecules.
   E) all of the above.

Answer: E

61) The general function of an enzyme in the body is to
    A) catalyze chemical reactions.
    B) maintain a neutral pH.
    C) act as a reactant in carbohydrate storage.
    D) maintain homeostasis.
    E) eliminate waste products from the blood.

Answer: A

62) "Physiologic conditions" for reactions within the body are approximately
    A) pH 3 and 37 °C.
    B) pH 7 and 37 °C.
    C) pH 7 and 37 °F.
    D) pH 8 and 273 °C.
    E) pH 7 and 273 K.

Answer: B

63) The hydrolysis of ester bonds in triacylglycerols is catalyzed by a
    A) lipase.
    B) lyase.
    C) isomerase.
    D) peptidase.
    E) oxidoreductase.

Answer: A

64) Most enzymes are
    A) fluid-mosaic proteins.
    B) induced proteins.
    C) substrate proteins.
    D) fibrous proteins.
    E) globular proteins.

Answer: E

65) In any reaction catalyzed by an enzyme, the reacting molecule is called the
    A) substrate.
    B) cofactor.
    C) coenzyme.
    D) isozyme.
    E) allostere.

Answer: A

66) The presence of enzymes to catalyze bioreactions in our bodies allows
    A) us to eat non-nutritious substances without consequence.
    B) the activation energy of a reaction to be raised.
    C) the rate of a desired chemical reaction to slow down.
    D) bioreactions to occur under extreme conditions of temperature and pH.
    E) bioreactions to take place under mild conditions.

Answer: E

67) "Physiological pH", the pH for optimum activity for most enzymes, is a pH equal to
    A) 3.0.   B) 5.4.   C) 7.4.   D) 8.6.   E) 9.0.

Answer: C

68) In the lock–and–key model of enzyme action, the enzyme active site is thought of as
   A) a rigid, nonflexible shape that fits the substrate exactly.
   B) an area of the enzyme that can adjust to fit the substrate shape.
   C) a key–like shape that fits into a pocket of the substrate surface.
   D) a hydrophilic area on the enzyme surface.
   E) a lock that bars a noncompetitive inhibitor from reacting.

   Answer: A

69) In the induced–fit model of enzyme action, the enzyme active site
   A) stays the same shape during substrate binding.
   B) adjusts shape to adapt to the shape of the substrate.
   C) stays the same shape while causing a change in the shape of the substrate.
   D) uses an inhibitor to adjust its shape for the substrate.
   E) uses a cofactor to change the shape of a substrate.

   Answer: B

70) The function of the enzyme–substrate complex is to provide an alternative reaction pathway
   that
   A) lowers the energy of the products.
   B) lowers the energy of the substrate.
   C) changes the concentration of the substrate.
   D) decreases the activation energy for the reaction.
   E) changes the possible product formed.

   Answer: D

71) How many generalized steps are there in the reaction of an enzyme (E) with a substrate (S) to
   form and release the product (P)?
   A) one   B) two   C) three   D) four   E) five

   Answer: B

72) Most enzymes are deactivated permanently above a temperature of about
   A) 25 °C.   B) 37 °F.   C) 40 °C.   D) 45 °F.   E) 50 °C.

   Answer: E

73) Urea is converted to ammonia and carbon dioxide by the action of urease. What will be the
   effect on the rate if the temperature of the reaction is lowered from 37 °C (the optimum
   temperature) to 27 °C?

$$\begin{array}{c} O \\ \| \\ NH_2\text{-}C\text{-}NH_2 \end{array} + H_2O \xrightarrow{\text{urease}} 2NH_3 + CO_2$$

   A) There will be no effect.
   B) The rate will slow down.
   C) The rate will double.
   D) The rate will triple.
   E) The rate will slow down, then speed up again.

   Answer: B

74) A competitive inhibitor is one that
    A) binds to the enzyme at a site far from the active site.
    B) binds to the active site in place of the substrate.
    C) destroys the substrate.
    D) binds to the allosteric site on an enzyme.
    E) forms a complex with the substrate.

    Answer: B

75) A noncompetitive inhibitor has a structure that
    A) does not resemble the substrate structure.
    B) resembles the active site of the enzyme.
    C) can bind to the active site of the enzyme.
    D) does not interfere with the enzyme-substrate complex formation.
    E) causes a change in the shape of the substrate.

    Answer: A

76) A compound that binds to the surface of an enzyme, and changes its shape so that a substrate cannot enter the active site, is called a(n)
    A) coenzyme
    B) proenzyme.
    C) cofactor.
    D) noncompetitive inhibitor.
    E) competitive inhibitor.

    Answer: D

77) The B vitamins are examples of
    A) water-soluble vitamins.
    B) essential amino acids.
    C) essential minerals.
    D) oil soluble vitamins.
    E) vitamins that are stored in the liver.

    Answer: A

78) Coenzymes such as water-soluble vitamins are needed in only small amounts because
    A) only small amounts of enzymes are present in each cell.
    B) only small amounts of substrates are available at any one time.
    C) they can be eliminated in the urine.
    D) each vitamin molecule can be reused many times as a cofactor.
    E) they can be stored in the liver for future use.

    Answer: D

79) A biological catalyst is called a(n) _____.
    A) lipid
    B) enzyme
    C) cofactor
    D) coenzyme
    E) substrate

    Answer: B

80) The full name of the enzyme LDH is _____.
   A) lactate dehydrogenase
   B) liver decompensation hexase
   C) lactate dehydrase
   D) liver dihydrogen kinase
   E) lipase dehydrogenase

   Answer: A

81) The names of many enzymes can be recognized by the suffix _____.
   A) –ate   B) –ite   C) –ose   D) –ine   E) –ase

   Answer: E

82) Enzymes that catalyze the same reactions but have slightly different structures are called _____.
   A) coenzymes
   B) cofactors
   C) isoenzymes
   D) competitive
   E) noncompetitive

   Answer: C

83) The optimum pH for the activity of pepsin is about _____.
   A) 2.0   B) 4.0   C) 6.5   D) 7.4   E) 7.6

   Answer: A

16.2 Bimodal Questions

1) Immunoglobulin, a protein that stimulates immune responses, would be classified as a _____ protein.
   A) transport
   B) structural
   C) storage
   D) protection
   E) catalytic

   Answer: D

2) In an enzyme, the polypeptide chain folds into a compact shape known as the _____ structure.
   A) pleated
   B) primary
   C) secondary
   D) tertiary
   E) quaternary

   Answer: D

3) What amino acids have polar side chains that are attracted to water?
   A) hydrophilic
   B) hydrophobic
   C) nonpolar
   D) aromatic
   E) hydrocarbon

   Answer: A

4) At what pH would you expect valine, an amino acid with a neutral side chain, to be in the zwitterionic form?
   A) 1   B) 4   C) 7   D) 10   E) 14

   Answer: C

5) Consider the R groups of the following amino acids:

   cysteine: –CH$_2$SH;   alanine: –CH$_3$;   serine: –CH$_2$OH

   The name for the dipeptide shown below is _____.

   $$\begin{array}{cccc} CH_3 & O & CH_2OH \\ | & || & | \\ NH_2\ C\ H\ -\ C\ -\ NH\ C\ HCOOH \end{array}$$

   A) alanyl–cysteine
   B) alanyl–serine
   C) seryl–alanine
   D) seryl–cysteine
   E) serine–alanine

   Answer: B

6) What process occurs when heat, acids, bases, and heavy metal ions cause a loss of biological function of a protein?
   A) denaturation
   B) saponification
   C) hydrogenation
   D) amidation
   E) esterification

   Answer: A

7) When two protein chains combine to form an active protein, the structural level is _____.
   A) pleated
   B) primary
   C) secondary
   D) tertiary
   E) quaternary

   Answer: E

8) Hydrophobic interactions help to stabilize the _____ structure(s) of a protein.
 A) primary
 B) secondary
 C) secondary and tertiary
 D) tertiary and quaternary
 E) secondary and quaternary
 Answer: D

16.3 Short Answer Questions

1) Collagen can be classified as a _____ protein.
 Answer: structural

2) The protein that transports oxygen in the blood is _____.
 Answer: hemoglobin

3) Proteins that stimulate immune response are known as _____.
 Answer: immunoglobulins

4) Amino acids that are not synthesized in the body but must be ingested with the diet are called _____ amino acids.
 Answer: essential

5) All naturally occurring amino acids in the human body are the _____ enantiomers.
 Answer: L–

6) A zwitterion of any amino acid has a net charge of _____.
 Answer: zero

7) The isoelectric point for any amino acid is the pH at which the amino acid has a net charge of _____.
 Answer: zero

8) Write the zwitterion of glycine.
 Answer:

$$\overset{+}{H_3N}-CH_2-\overset{\displaystyle \overset{O}{\|}}{C}-O^-$$

9) Circle the peptide bond in this structure.

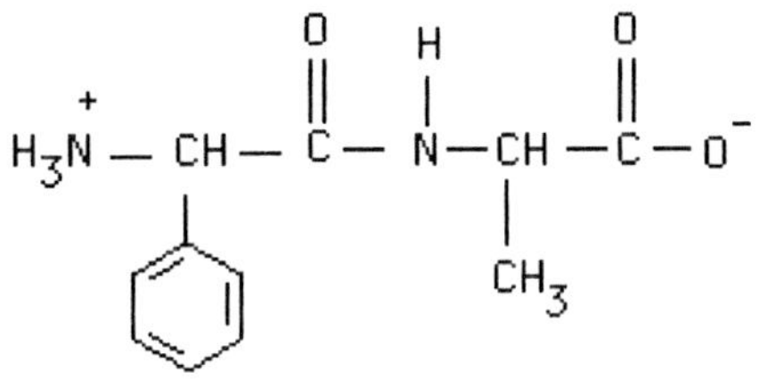

Answer:

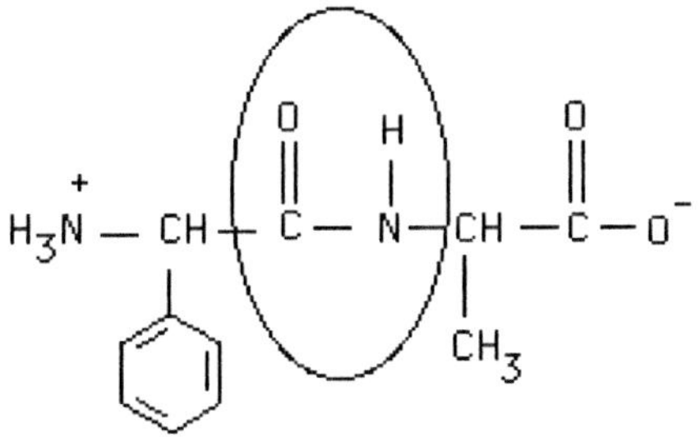

Indicate whether each of the following is fat soluble or water soluble.

10) vitamin B_6

Answer: water soluble

11) vitamin A

Answer: fat soluble

12) pantothenic acid

Answer: water soluble

13) ascorbic acid

Answer: water soluble

14) vitamin E

Answer: fat soluble

15) vitamin K

Answer: fat soluble

16) niacin

Answer: water soluble

17) folic acid

Answer: water soluble

18) vitamin D

Answer: fat soluble

19) riboflavin

Answer: water soluble

16.4 Matching Questions

Identify the structural level in each protein.

1) The protein folds into a compact structure stabilized by interactions between R groups.

2) the combination of two or more protein molecules to form an active protein

3) pleated sheet

4) the peptide bonds between the amino acids

5) the structural level achieved when hydrogen bonds form between the carboxyl group of one amino acid and the amino group of a different amino acid

A) secondary structure

B) primary structure

C) quaternary

D) tertiary

1) D   2) C   3) A   4) B   5) A

Would an amino acid with the given side chain be most likely to be found in the hydrophobic or hydrophilic region of a protein?

6) $-CH_2 - CH - CH_3$
$\quad\quad\quad |$
$\quad\quad\quad CH_3$

7) $- CH - CH_3$
$\quad\quad |$
$\quad\quad OH$

8) $-CH_3$

9) $-CH_2-CH_2-S-CH_3$

10)
$\quad\quad\quad\quad\quad O$
$\quad\quad\quad\quad\quad ||$
$\quad - CH_2 - C - NH_2$

A) both

B) hydrophobic

C) hydrophilic

11)

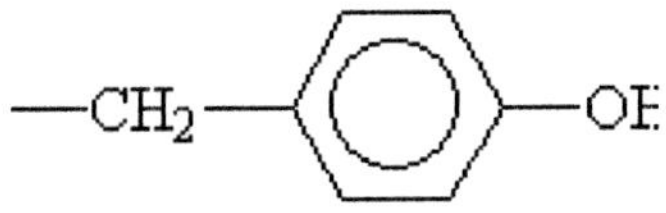

$-CH_2-$⟨benzene ring⟩$-OH$

12) $-CH-CH_2-CH_3$
$\quad\;\;|$
$\quad\;\;CH_3$

13)

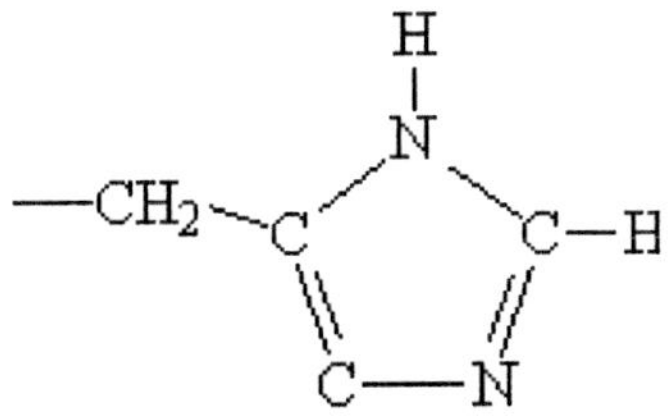

$-CH_2-C$ (imidazole ring with N-H, C-H, C-N)

14)

$-CH_2-$⟨benzene ring⟩

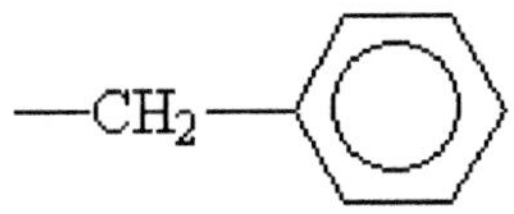

6) B	7) C	8) B	9) B	10) C	11) C
12) B	13) C	14) B			

Classify each protein by function.

15) trypsin for the hydrolysis of protein

16) lipoproteins in the blood

17) collagen in tendons and cartilage

18) antibodies

19) actin in muscle

A) catalytic

B) protection

C) structural

D) contractile

E) transport

15) A	16) E	17) C	18) B	19) D

Identify each of the designated regions on the energy diagram for the conversion of a substrate to product with and without an enzyme.

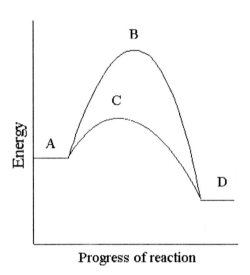

20) energy of the substrate   A) Region D

21) energy of the product   B) Region B

22) activation energy without the   C) Region A
     enzyme
                                  D) Region C

23) activation energy with the
     enzyme

20) C   21) A   22) B   23) D

Match the correct term in enzyme action with each description.

24) the temporary combination of   A) lock–and–key theory
     an enzyme with the
     compound on which it acts   B) enzyme–substrate complex

25) an organic compound that is   C) cofactor
     sometimes needed to
     complete an enzyme   D) active site

26) the portion of an enzyme   E) coenzyme
     molecule where catalytic
     activity occurs

27) an inorganic substance such
     as Mg^{2+} required by some
     enzymes for activity

28) one theory that accounts for
     the unusual specificity of an
     enzyme

24) B   25) E   26) D   27) C   28) A

Identify the effect of the following on the activity of maltase, an enzyme that hydrolyzes maltose.

29) decreasing the concentration   A) has no effect
   of maltose

                                            B) increases
30) adjusting the temperature to
   the optimum temperature   C) decreases

31) raising the pH to 11.0

32) increasing the concentration
   of maltase (enzyme) when the
   enzyme is saturated with
   substrate

33) lowering the pH to 1.0

29) C   30) B   31) C   32) B   33) C

Identify the type of inhibition in each description.

34) an inhibitor that resembles the   A) competitive
   structure of the substrate

                                            B) noncompetitive
35) Adding more substrate does
   not reverse the effect of this
   inhibitor.

36) The inhibition can be reversed
   by increasing the
   concentration of substrate.

37) The inhibitor does not
   resemble the substrate.

34) A   35) B   36) A   37) B

Chapter 17 Nucleic Acids and Protein Synthesis

17.1 Multiple-Choice Questions

1) A _____ consists of a nitrogen–containing base and a sugar.
   A) nucleoside
   B) base pair
   C) nucleotide
   D) complementary base
   E) pyrimidine

   Answer: A

2) A _____ consists of a nitrogen–containing base, a sugar, and a phosphate group.
   A) nucleoside
   B) base pair
   C) nucleotide
   D) complementary base
   E) purine

   Answer: C

3) Which of the following can NOT be found in a nucleotide of RNA?
   A) purine
   B) pyrimidine
   C) phosphate
   D) ribose
   E) deoxyribose

   Answer: E

4) Which of the following is found in RNA but not in DNA?
   A) thymine
   B) uracil
   C) guanine
   D) cytosine
   E) deoxyribose

   Answer: B

5) Which of the following will not be found in DNA?
   A) adenine   B) thymine   C) guanine   D) cytosine   E) ribose

   Answer: E

6) Which of the following can be found in DNA?
   A) ribose
   B) GMP
   C) uracil
   D) deoxyadenosine
   E) FMN

   Answer: D

7) The nucleotides in the backbone of DNA are held together by _____ bonds.
   A) hydrogen
   B) peptide
   C) phosphodiester
   D) glycosidic
   E) ionic
   Answer: C

8) The bonds that link the base pairs in the DNA double helix are
   A) ionic bonds.
   B) peptide bonds.
   C) hydrogen bonds.
   D) hydrophobic bonds.
   E) ester bonds.
   Answer: C

9) The base sequence of the strand of DNA complementary to the segment
   –T–G–G–C–A–A–C– is:
   A) –T–G–G–C–A–A–C–
   B) –A–C–C–G–T–T–G–
   C) –A–C–C–G–U–U–G–
   D) –U–C–C–G–T–T–G–
   E) –A–C–G–C–T–U–G–
   Answer: B

10) The two new DNA molecules formed in replication
    A) are different from the original DNA.
    B) both contain only two new daughter DNA strands.
    C) both contain only the parent DNA strands.
    D) contain one parent and one daughter strand.
    E) are identical, with one containing both parent strands, and the other containing both
       daughter strands.
    Answer: D

11) What is the process in which the DNA double helix unfolds, and each strand serves as a
    template for the synthesis of a new strand?
    A) transcription
    B) complementation
    C) translation
    D) replication
    E) restriction
    Answer: D

12) When DNA replicates, a guanine forms a base pair with
    A) uracil.   B) adenine.   C) guanine.   D) thymine.   E) cytosine.
    Answer: E

13) Which of the following types of RNA carries the genetic information from DNA in the nucleus to the ribosomes?
A) mRNA
B) histone RNA
C) rRNA
D) tRNA
E) sRNA
Answer: A

14) Translation is the process whereby
A) DNA is synthesized from DNA.
B) DNA is synthesized from mRNA.
C) protein is synthesized from DNA.
D) protein is synthesized from mRNA.
E) mRNA is synthesized from DNA.
Answer: D

15) In transcription
A) the mRNA produced is identical to the parent DNA.
B) a double helix containing one parent strand and one daughter strand is produced.
C) uracil pairs with thymine.
D) both strands of the DNA are copied.
E) the mRNA produced is complementary to one strand of the DNA.
Answer: E

16) Which of the following is a section of mRNA produced from the DNA template below?

–A–T–A–G–C–T–A–

A) –A–T–A–G–C–T–A–
B) –A–U–A–G–C–U–A–
C) –U–A–U–C–G–A–U–
D) –U–U–U–G–C–U–U–
E) –T–A–T–C–G–A–T–
Answer: C

17) Which one of the following base pairs is found in DNA?
A) adenine–thymine
B) adenine–guanine
C) cytosine–thymine
D) adenine–uracil
E) guanine–uracil
Answer: A

18) In the synthesis of mRNA, an adenine in the DNA pairs with
A) uracil.   B) adenine.   C) guanine.   D) thymine.   E) cytosine.
Answer: A

19) A DNA template having the base sequence –A–G–A–T–G–A– would produce a mRNA with a base sequence of
    A) –A–G–A–T–G–A–.
    B) –U–C–U–A–C–U–.
    C) –T–C–T–U–C–T–.
    D) –T–C–T–A–C–A–.
    E) –A–C–A–U–C–A–.

Answer: B

20) Codons are base pair sequences that
    A) signal the start of DNA synthesis.
    B) signal the end of DNA synthesis.
    C) code for amino acids.
    D) signal the start of RNA synthesis.
    E) code for one or more bases in mRNA.

Answer: C

21) When mRNA is synthesized using the information from DNA, the process is called
    A) transportation.
    B) transposition.
    C) transcription.
    D) translation.
    E) transliteration.

Answer: C

22) The codon is found on _____, and the anticodon is found on _____.
    A) mRNA, tRNA
    B) tRNA, mRNA
    C) rRNA, tRNA
    D) ribosomes, tRNA
    E) mRNA, rRNA

Answer: A

23) The anticodon is
    A) identical to the codon on DNA.
    B) complementary to the codon on DNA.
    C) identical to the codon on mRNA.
    D) complementary to the codon on mRNA.
    E) complementary to the codon on tRNA.

Answer: D

24) During protein synthesis, the codon for an amino acid is found on
    A) DNA.   B) rRNA.   C) tRNA.   D) mRNA.   E) sRNA.

Answer: D

25) The anticodon of –U–A–G– is
    A) –A–T–C–.
    B) –U–A–G–.
    C) –A–A–C–.
    D) –A–U–C–.
    E) –G–A–U–.

    Answer: D

26) Mutations are the result of
    A) alterations in the phosphate of the DNA backbone.
    B) exposure to water in utero.
    C) physical trauma in the mother's childhood.
    D) alterations in the sugar component of the DNA backbone.
    E) alterations in the DNA base sequence.

    Answer: E

27) The result of a defective enzyme caused by a mutation in the DNA nucleotide sequence is
    A) a genetic disease.
    B) AIDS.
    C) HIV.
    D) recombinant DNA.
    E) translocation.

    Answer: A

28) A set of directions in the DNA base sequence for the synthesis of a protein is a(n)
    A) structural gene.
    B) promotor.
    C) operator.
    D) codon.
    E) regulatory gene.

    Answer: A

29) Small living particles, with 3 to 200 genes, that cannot replicate without a host cell are called
    A) recombinant DNAs.
    B) viruses.
    C) bacteria.
    D) tumors.
    E) plasmids.

    Answer: B

30) A virus that contains RNA as its genetic material is a
    A) genetically engineered virus.
    B) bacteria.
    C) recombinant DNA.
    D) retrovirus.
    E) vaccine.

    Answer: D

31) Protease inhibitors, which are effective anti–HIV drugs,
    A) are nucleoside analogs.
    B) prevent reverse transcription.
    C) prevent synthesis of viral proteins.
    D) prevent mRNA synthesis.
    E) prevent activation of tRNA.

Answer: C

32) The two strands of the double helix of DNA are held together by
    A) hydrogen bonds.
    B) covalent bonds.
    C) dipole–dipole interactions.
    D) ionic bonds.
    E) sugar–to–phosphate bonds.

Answer: A

33) When a mutation occurs by elimination of one base in a DNA sequence, this mutation is called
a
    A) frame–shift mutation.
    B) retrovirus insertion.
    C) substitution mutation.
    D) translocation mutation.
    E) viral mutation.

Answer: A

34) A mutation which occurs when one base in a DNA sequence replaces another, is called a
    A) frame–shift mutation.
    B) retrovirus insertion.
    C) substitution mutation.
    D) translocation mutation.
    E) viral mutation.

Answer: C

17.2 True/False Questions

1) Adenine is a purine.
   Answer: TRUE

2) Uracil is a pyrimidine.
   Answer: TRUE

3) AZT is a drug used in the treatment of cancer.
   Answer: FALSE

4) A retrovirus uses DNA as its genetic material.
   Answer: FALSE

5) A nucleotide consists of only a base and a sugar.
   Answer: FALSE

6) Down syndrome is an acquired disease, not a genetic disease.
   Answer: FALSE

7) Messenger RNA carries protein synthesis information from the nucleus to the ribosomes.
   Answer: TRUE

8) The DNA complement of the sequence –GCCAT– is –GCCAT–.
   Answer: FALSE

9) DNA is a protein.
   Answer: FALSE

10) DNA differs from RNA in the sugar it contains.
    Answer: TRUE

11) mRNA codons contain three "letters."
    Answer: TRUE

12) The stop codon terminates protein synthesis.
    Answer: TRUE

13) In the DNA double helix, a purine can only bond with a pyrimidine.
    Answer: TRUE

17.3 Matching Questions

Match the following.

1) picks up the specific amino   A) mRNA
   acids for protein synthesis
                                       B) DNA
2) synthesized by the DNA to
   carry the genetic message to   C) tRNA
   the ribosomes
                                       D) rRNA
3) contains within the nucleus of
   the cell the information for the
   synthesis of protein

4) the nucleic acid that contains
   the codons for the amino
   acids of a protein

5) the most abundant nucleic
   acid in the ribosomes

6) the nucleic acid that contains
   a single anticodon for a
   specific amino acid

1) C   2) A   3) B   4) A   5) D   6) C

Chapter 18 Metabolic Pathways and Energy Production

18.1 Multiple-Choice Questions

1) Which coenzyme is the electron acceptor in the following reaction?

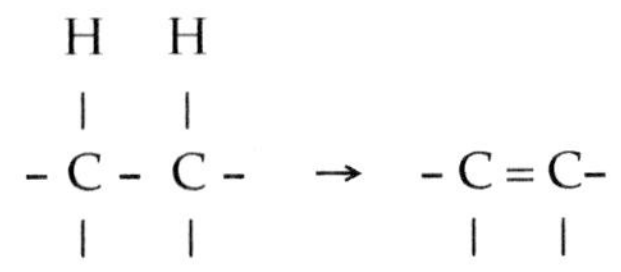

```
   H   H
   |   |
 - C - C -    →    - C = C-
   |   |              |   |
```

   A) FAD   B) NAD⁺   C) FMN   D) NADH   E) FADH₂

   Answer: A

2) Which coenzyme is the electron acceptor in the following reaction?

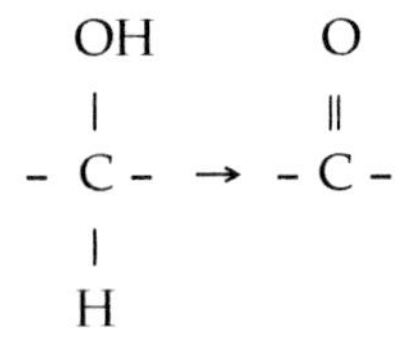

```
   OH       O
   |        ‖
 - C -  →  - C -
   |
   H
```

   A) FAD   B) NAD⁺   C) FMN   D) NADH   E) FADH₂

   Answer: B

3) Which of the following metabolic pathways can occur in the absence of oxygen?
   A) electron transport
   B) oxidative phosphorylation
   C) citric acid cycle
   D) glycolysis
   E) β-oxidation

   Answer: D

4) In step 7 of glycolysis, ATP is generated when a phosphate group is transferred directly from 1,3-bisphosphoglycerate to ADP in a process known as
   A) oxidation.
   B) substrate level phosphorylation.
   C) reduction.
   D) transamination.
   E) oxidative phosphorylation.

   Answer: B

5) The compounds formed when fructose-1, 6-bisphosphate is split are
    A) pyruvic acid and lactic acid.
    B) ethanol and acetyl CoA.
    C) dihydroxyacetone phosphate and pyruvic acid.
    D) dihydroxyacetone phosphate and glyceraldehyde-3-phosphate.
    E) glyceraldehyde 3-phosphate and pyruvic acid.

Answer: D

6) When one glucose molecule undergoes glycolysis it generates
    A) 6 ATP.
    B) 6 ATP and 2 NADH.
    C) 2 ATP and 2 NADH.
    D) 2 ATP and 4 NADH.
    E) 12 ATP.

Answer: C

7) The process by which complex molecules are broken down into simpler ones for the body's use is called
    A) metabolism.
    B) catabolism.
    C) anabolism.
    D) glucogenesis.
    E) gluconeogenesis.

Answer: B

8) The process of building up new molecules in the cell is called
    A) metabolism.
    B) catabolism.
    C) anabolism.
    D) glycolysis.
    E) transamination.

Answer: C

9) Overall, catabolic reactions
    A) release energy.
    B) take in energy.
    C) occur mainly in the liver.
    D) occur outside the cell membrane.
    E) take place in the nucleus of the cell.

Answer: A

10) Anabolic reactions are reactions that
    A) use oxidation but not reduction.
    B) break down large molecules into smaller ones.
    C) take place in the mitochondria.
    D) use energy.
    E) give off energy.

Answer: D

11) How many main stages of catabolism are there?
   A) one   B) two   C) three   D) four   E) five

   Answer: C

12) The first stage of catabolism is
   A) the citric acid cycle.
   B) production of pyruvate.
   C) production of acetyl CoA.
   D) buildup of macromolecules from monomers.
   E) digestion of large molecules.

   Answer: E

13) The middle stage of catabolism is the point at which
   A) acetyl CoA is produced.
   B) monomers are produced from macromolecules.
   C) macromolecules are made from monomers.
   D) glycogen is converted to glucose.
   E) excess nutrients are stored as fats.

   Answer: A

14) Protein synthesis takes place
   A) in the mitochondria.
   B) on the endoplasmic reticulum.
   C) in the nucleus.
   D) on the ribosomes.
   E) in the cytosol.

   Answer: D

15) The main compound used to release energy for metabolism is
   A) sucrose.
   B) glucose phosphate.
   C) adenosine triphosphate.
   D) ribonucleic acid.
   E) NAD^+.

   Answer: C

16) The components of ATP are
   A) adenosine, ribose, and triphosphate.
   B) aniline and triphosphate.
   C) alanine, ribose, and triphosphate.
   D) adenine, ribose, and triphosphate.
   E) adenosine, deoxyribose, and triphosphate.

   Answer: D

17) The hydrolysis of ATP to ADP is
   A) endothermic.
   B) exothermic.
   C) isothermic.
   D) an oxidation.
   E) a reduction.

   Answer: B

18) The final products of catabolic reactions are
    A) carbon dioxide, water, and ammonia.
    B) glucose, lipids, and glycogen.
    C) lipids, oxygen, and water.
    D) RNA and DNA.
    E) lipids and carbohydrates.

Answer: A

19) In biochemical systems, the term *reduction* often refers to
    A) a loss of hydrogen or electrons by a compound.
    B) a gain of hydrogen or electrons by a compound.
    C) a gain in oxygen.
    D) a loss of electrons.
    E) an energy-releasing reaction.

Answer: B

20) NAD^+ participates in reactions that produce
    A) a CH_2 group.
    B) a C=O bond.
    C) phosphorylation.
    D) ADP from ATP.
    E) a C-C bond.

Answer: B

21) FAD is a coenzyme which usually participates in
    A) oxidation of alcohols to aldehydes.
    B) formation of carbon-carbon double bonds.
    C) decarboxylation reactions.
    D) phosphorylation reactions.
    E) β-oxidation reactions.

Answer: B

22) Coenzyme A is a molecule whose function is to
    A) activate enzyme A.
    B) undergo phosphorylation.
    C) provide energy for the citric acid cycle.
    D) activate acyl groups for reaction.
    E) help break down macromolecules.

Answer: D

23) Digestion of carbohydrates begins in the
    A) mouth.
    B) stomach.
    C) pancreas.
    D) small intestine.
    E) large intestine.

Answer: A

24) An enzyme that can facilitate the breakdown of starch into smaller units is
   A) glucose phosphatase.
   B) alcohol dehydrogenase.
   C) amylase.
   D) lactase.
   E) maltase.
   Answer: C

25) Glycolysis is a(n) _____ process.
   A) aerobic   B) anaerobic   C) anabolic   D) one-step   E) five-step
   Answer: B

26) In the process of glycolysis, glucose is converted to
   A) pyruvate.
   B) citrate.
   C) sucrose.
   D) oxaloacetate.
   E) ribose.
   Answer: A

27) The overall process of glycolysis
   A) requires oxygen.
   B) uses up 4 ATP molecules.
   C) requires acetyl CoA.
   D) is an anabolic pathway.
   E) produces 2 ATP molecules.
   Answer: E

28) Under aerobic conditions, pyruvate produced in glycolysis can be converted to
   A) glyceraldehyde-3-phosphate.
   B) lactic acid.
   C) glucose-6-phosphate.
   D) fructose-6-phosphate.
   E) acetyl CoA.
   Answer: E

29) Under anaerobic conditions, lactate is produced from
   A) acetyl CoA.
   B) pyruvate.
   C) ATP.
   D) carbon dioxide.
   E) NAD^+.
   Answer: B

30) When combined with the electron transport chain, one turn of the citric acid cycle produces
   _____ ATP.
   A) 24   B) 12   C) 11   D) 14   E) 2
   Answer: B

31) What is the correct coefficient for ATP in the complete combustion of glucose?

$$C_6H_{12}O_6 + 6O_2 \rightarrow 6CO_2 + \underline{\quad} ATP + 6H_2O$$

    A) 6   B) 12   C) 18   D) 24   E) 36

Answer: E

32) In the absence of oxygen in muscles, pyruvate is converted to
    A) glycogen.
    B) glucose.
    C) ethanol.
    D) lactate.
    E) glyceraldehyde-3-phosphate.

Answer: D

33) Under anaerobic conditions, there is a net production of _____ ATP during glycolysis.
    A) zero   B) two   C) four   D) six   E) eight

Answer: B

34) In order to enter the citric acid cycle, pyruvate is first converted to
    A) lactate.
    B) acetaldehyde.
    C) citrate.
    D) acetyl CoA.
    E) ethanol.

Answer: D

35) The citric acid cycle is used in the oxidation of
    A) glucose only.
    B) glucose and fatty acids only.
    C) fatty acids only.
    D) glucose, fatty acids, and proteins.
    E) proteins only.

Answer: D

36) What electron acceptor(s) is(are) used in the citric acid cycle?
    A) FAD only
    B) NAD^+ only
    C) $NADH + FADH_2 + CoA$
    D) FMN
    E) $NAD^+ + FAD$

Answer: E

37) Which of the following compounds in the citric acid cycle undergoes oxidative decarboxylation?
   A) citrate
   B) isocitrate
   C) succinate
   D) fumarate
   E) succinyl CoA

Answer: B

38) The citric acid cycle operates only under aerobic conditions because
   A) oxygen is a reactant in the citric acid cycle.
   B) oxygen is a product of the citric acid cycle.
   C) CO_2 is a product of the citric acid cycle.
   D) the NADH and $FADH_2$ produced by the citric acid cycle can only be reoxidized by the electron transport chain.
   E) the NAD^+ and FAD produced by the citric acid cycle can only be reduced by the electron transport chain.

Answer: D

39) In the chemiosmotic model of oxidative phosphorylation, ATP is synthesized as
   A) OH^- flows through ATP synthase.
   B) electrons flow through ATP synthase.
   C) Ca^{2+} flows through ATP synthase.
   D) H^+ flows through ATP synthase.
   E) Na^+ flows through ATP synthase.

Answer: D

40) The components of the electron transport chain do NOT include
   A) oxygen (O_2).
   B) cytochromes.
   C) FMN.
   D) CoQ.
   E) acetyl CoA.

Answer: E

41) In the electron transport chain, the synthesis of ATP from ADP + P_i is called
   A) glycolysis.
   B) acylation.
   C) oxidative phosphorylation.
   D) isomerization.
   E) hydrolysis.

Answer: C

42) In the electron transport chain, the oxidized product from the reaction of FMN + NADH + H^+ is
   A) CoQ.   B) $FMNH_2$.   C) FADH.   D) FAD.   E) NAD^+.

Answer: E

43) The electron carrier _____ provides two ATP via the electron transport chain.
    A) $FADH_2$ B) NADH   C) NADPH   D) CoASH   E) $FNMH_2$

Answer: A

44) When oxygen is in plentiful supply in the cell, pyruvate is converted to
    A) CoA.
    B) acetyl CoA.
    C) glucose.
    D) lactate.
    E) fructose.

Answer: B

45) Which of the three major stages of metabolism includes the citric acid cycle?
    A) stage one   B) stage two   C) stage three

Answer: C

46) The citric acid cycle takes place in the
    A) mitochondria.
    B) cytosol.
    C) cytoplasm.
    D) Golgi apparatus.
    E) endoplasmic reticulum.

Answer: A

47) In stage three of metabolism, the overall result is to release
    A) glucose and water.
    B) lactate and acetyl CoA.
    C) lactate and glucose.
    D) glycogen and water.
    E) carbon dioxide and energy.

Answer: E

48) Most of the energy released in the citric acid cycle is used to produce
    A) glucose.
    B) acetyl CoA.
    C) NADH and $FADH_2$.
    D) carbon dioxide and water.
    E) citric acid.

Answer: C

49) In the electron transport chain, NADH and $FADH_2$ are used to provide
    A) oxygen.
    B) electrons and hydrogen ions.
    C) carbon atoms.
    D) water and carbon dioxide.
    E) thiol groups.

Answer: B

50) The energy released during the electron transport chain is used to produce
    A) glucose.
    B) citric acid.
    C) carbon dioxide.
    D) ATP.
    E) NADH.

Answer: D

51) In the first reaction of the citric acid cycle
    A) glucose becomes pyruvate.
    B) ATP is produced.
    C) NADH is produced.
    D) acetyl CoA reacts with oxaloacetate to give citrate.
    E) pyruvate becomes CO_2 and H_2O.

Answer: D

52) The citric acid cycle step that removes the first CO_2 molecule is a(n)
    A) oxidative decarboxylation.
    B) reduction.
    C) carbonylation.
    D) hydrolysis.
    E) combination.

Answer: A

53) In the third major step of the citric acid cycle, NAD^+ is converted to
    A) NAS^-.   B) NAD^{2+}.   C) $NADH_2$.   D) NAD.   E) NADH.

Answer: E

54) Step 5 of the citric acid cycle is the hydrolysis of succinyl coA. In this reaction
    A) the energy released is used to make GTP.
    B) the energy released is used to make ATP.
    C) carbon dioxide is released.
    D) α–ketoglutarate is released.
    E) the enzyme aconitase is needed.

Answer: A

55) The GTP formed in step 5 of the citric acid cycle is used to make
    A) carbon dioxide.
    B) oxygen.
    C) water.
    D) CoA.
    E) ATP.

Answer: E

56) In the dehydrogenation of succinate to fumarate in the citric acid cycle, the coenzyme used is
    A) CoA.
    B) acetyl CoA.
    C) NAD^+.
    D) NADH.
    E) FAD.

Answer: E

57) In step 7 of the citric acid cycle, fumarate is converted to malate by a _____ reaction.
    A) hydrolysis
    B) dehydrogenation
    C) hydrogenation
    D) hydration
    E) dehydration

Answer: D

58) The last step in the citric acid cycle converts malate to
    A) citrate.
    B) isocitrate.
    C) succinate.
    D) fumarate.
    E) oxaloacetate.

Answer: E

59) Overall, one turn of the citric acid cycle produces
    A) three CO_2 molecules.
    B) three NADH molecules.
    C) two $FADH_2$ molecules.
    D) 6 ATP.
    E) 2 GTP.

Answer: B

60) The compounds in electron transport that rermove hydrogen ions and electrons from NADH are classified as
    A) oxidative transporters.
    B) osmotic carriers.
    C) electron carriers.
    D) phosphorylators.
    E) citrates.

Answer: C

61) One example of an electron carrier in the respiratory chain is
    A) ATP.
    B) GTP.
    C) coenzyme Q.
    D) citrate.
    E) water.

Answer: C

62) In the chemiosmotic model, protons circulate through a protein complex called
   A) iron–sulfur clusters.
   B) FMA.
   C) CoA.
   D) CoQ.
   E) ATP synthase.

   Answer: E

63) In glycolysis, glucose produces 2 pyruvate molecules and a total of _____ ATP molecules.
   A) 2   B) 4   C) 6   D) 8   E) 12

   Answer: C

64) The complete oxidation of glucose produces _____ ATP molecules.
   A) 2   B) 8   C) 12   D) 24   E) 36

   Answer: E

65) In the activation of a fatty acid, energy from the hydrolysis of ATP is used to
   A) form a double bond in an oxidation reaction.
   B) join the fatty acid to CoA.
   C) add a molecule of water across a double bond to give a hydroxyl group on the β-carbon.
   D) oxidize the hydroxyl group on the β-carbon.
   E) cause a unit of acetyl CoA to separate from the fatty acid chain.

   Answer: B

66) The coenzyme(s) used in fatty acid synthesis is (are) _____.
   A) NADH
   B) $FADH_2$
   C) NADPH
   D) NADH and NADPH
   E) $FADH_2$ and NADH

   Answer: C

67) The series of reactions that produces energy by hydrolyzing fats to units of acetyl CoA is called
   A) transamination.
   B) β-oxidation.
   C) hydration.
   D) hydrolysis.
   E) β-reduction.

   Answer: B

68) Which step is found in the breakdown of a fat?
   A) an activation that requires 2 ATP.
   B) an oxidation with a cytochrome.
   C) an oxidation with CoQ.
   D) direct substrate phosphorylation.
   E) production of pyruvate.

   Answer: A

69) During complete oxidation of the fatty acid $CH_3-(CH_2)_{18}-COOH$, _____ molecules of acetyl CoA are produced, and the fatty acid goes through the β-oxidation cycle _____ times.
    A) ten, ten
    B) nine, ten
    C) nine, nine
    D) nine, eight
    E) ten, nine
    Answer: E

70) What is the total number of ATP molecules produced from the lauric acid $(C_{12}H_{24}O_2)$ found in coconut oil?
    A) 72 ATP   B) 90 ATP   C) 100 ATP   D) 97 ATP   E) 95 ATP
    Answer: E

71) The complete oxidation of $CH_3-(CH_2)_8-COOH$ produces _____ molecules of ATP.
    A) 80   B) 78   C) 82   D) 74   E) 76
    Answer: B

72) In a(n) _____ reaction, NH_4^+ is produced when glutamate is converted to α-ketoglutarate.

    A) dehydrogenation
    B) transamination
    C) oxidative deamination
    D) reduction
    E) hydration
    Answer: C

73) Which of the following does NOT require NAD^+?
    A) glycolysis
    B) transamination
    C) citric acid cycle
    D) β-oxidation
    E) oxidative deamination
    Answer: B

74) In mammals, the ammonium ion produced in oxidative deamination is
    A) excreted in the feces.
    B) stored in the liver.
    C) converted to uric acid, which is excreted in the urine.
    D) converted to urea, which is excreted in the urine.
    E) converted to uric acid, which is excreted by the liver.
    Answer: D

75) The digestion of protein begins in the
    A) mouth.
    B) stomach.
    C) small intestine.
    D) large intestine.
    E) pancreas.
    Answer: B

76) The initial digestion of protein is catalyzed by an enzyme called
    A) chymotrypsin.
    B) peptidase.
    C) pepsin.
    D) amylase.
    E) trypsin.
    Answer: C

77) The digestion of fats begins in the
    A) mouth.
    B) stomach.
    C) small intestine.
    D) gall bladder.
    E) large intestine.
    Answer: C

78) The digestion of fats begins when the fat globules are
    A) emulsified by bile salts.
    B) attacked by protease enzymes to form smaller fat globules.
    C) converted to lipoproteins for greater solubility.
    D) hydrolyzed to glucose and amino acids.
    E) hydrolyzed to glycerol and fatty acids.
    Answer: A

79) The primary fuel for the synthesis of ATP is
    A) protein.
    B) lactate.
    C) ammonia.
    D) GTP.
    E) glucose.
    Answer: E

80) Fatty acids and glycerol are produced from the metabolism of
    A) lipids.
    B) proteins.
    C) carbohydrates.
    D) amino acids.
    E) glucose.
    Answer: A

81) The action of pancreatic lipase on triacylglycerols produces
    A) emulsions.
    B) micelles.
    C) monoacylglycerols and free fatty acids.
    D) high-density lipoproteins.
    E) low-density lipoproteins.
    Answer: C

82) A chylomicron is a
   A) lipase.
   B) digestive enzyme.
   C) triacylglycerol.
   D) transport lipoprotein.
   E) storage protein.

Answer: D

83) The enzymes that break down triacylglycerols into fatty acids and glycerol are called
   A) lyases.
   B) aconitases.
   C) lipases.
   D) hydrolases.
   E) oxidoreductases.

Answer: C

84) The removal of 2-carbon segments of a fatty acid for further metabolism is called
   A) β-oxidation.
   B) transamination.
   C) deglyceration.
   D) dehydration.
   E) decarboxylation.

Answer: A

85) The 2-carbon segments removed from a fatty acid during metabolism are used to form
   A) glucose.
   B) pyruvate.
   C) lactate.
   D) CoA.
   E) acetyl CoA.

Answer: E

86) The 2-carbon units obtained by degradation of a fatty acid are further metabolized in
   A) oxidative deamination.
   B) the citric acid cycle.
   C) β-oxidation.
   D) glycolysis.
   E) transamination.

Answer: B

87) Myristic acid, a C_{14} fatty acid, produces _____ acetyl CoA when completely metabolized.
   A) 2   B) 5   C) 7   D) 12   E) 14

Answer: C

88) Myristic acid, a C_{14} fatty acid, undergoes the β-oxidation cycle _____ times.
   A) 2   B) 4   C) 6   D) 7   E) 14

Answer: C

89) Each acetyl CoA produces _____ ATP in the citric acid cycle.
   A) 2   B) 6   C) 10   D) 12   E) 24

Answer: D

90) Ketosis is a condition that can occur if
   A) ketone bodies cannot be completely metabolized.
   B) too many ketones are ingested.
   C) too much protein is available in the diet.
   D) the brain is starved of glucose.
   E) low fat intake occurs.

   Answer: A

91) Ketosis can lower the blood pH below 7.4, producing the condition
   A) anemia.
   B) hyponatremia.
   C) hypokalemia.
   D) acidosis.
   E) alkalosis.

   Answer: D

18.2 Bimodal Questions

1) This is the term that refers to all of the chemical reactions in living cells.
   A) glycolysis
   B) β-oxidation
   C) metabolism
   D) anabolism
   E) catabolism

   Answer: C

2) The energy for most energy–requiring reactions in the cells of the body is obtained by the hydrolysis of _____.
   A) ATP
   B) ADP
   C) AMP
   D) cyclic AMP
   E) GTP

   Answer: A

3) Most of the energy in our bodies is stored in the form of _____.
   A) glycogen
   B) glucose
   C) proteins
   D) triacylglycerols
   E) cholesterol

   Answer: D

4) Hydrolysis of sucrose takes place primarily in the _____.
   A) mouth
   B) stomach
   C) pancreas
   D) small intestine
   E) large intestine

   Answer: D

5) The net energy production in anaerobic glycolysis is _____.
   A) 2 ATP   B) 4 ATP   C) 6 ATP   D) 8 ATP   E) 12 ATP
   Answer: A

6) Most of the energy in the typical animal cell is produced in the _____.
   A) cytosol
   B) nucleus
   C) mitochondria
   D) lysosomes
   E) endoplasmic reticulum
   Answer: C

18.3 Short Answer Questions

In this figure taken from your text, identify the metabolic substance numbered.

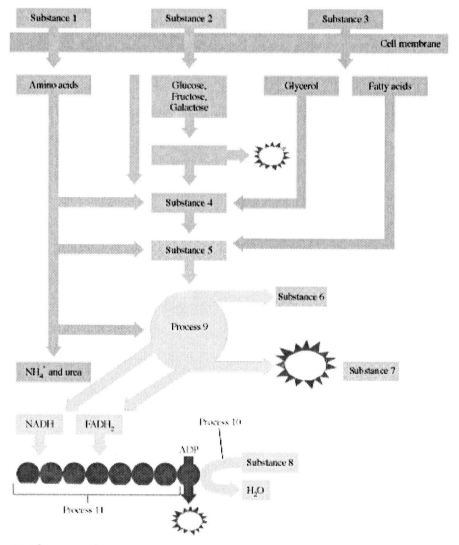

1) substance 2

   Answer: carbohydrates or polysaccharides

2) substance 3

    Answer: lipids

3) substance 4

    Answer: pyruvate

4) substance 5

    Answer: acetyl CoA

5) substance 6

    Answer: carbon dioxide

6) substance 7

    Answer: ATP

7) substance 8

    Answer: oxygen

8) process 9

    Answer: citric acid cycle or Krebs cycle or tricarboxylic acid cycle

9) process 10

    Answer: electron transport

10) process 11

    Answer: oxidative phosphorylation

In this figure taken from your text, identify the substances shown.

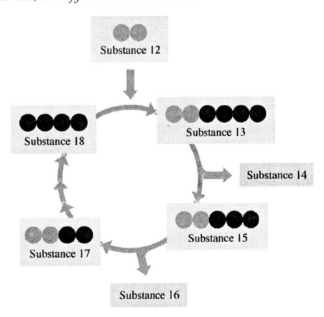

11) substance 12

    Answer: acetyl CoA

12) substance 13

Answer: citrate

13) substance 14

Answer: carbon dioxide

14) substance 15

Answer: α-ketoglutarate

15) substance 16

Answer: carbon dioxide

16) substance 17

Answer: succinyl CoA

17) substance 18

Answer: oxaloacetate

18.4 True/False Questions

1) Energy production in the cell occurs primarily in the nucleus.
Answer: FALSE

2) The cytosol is an aqueous solution of salts and enzymes.
Answer: TRUE

3) Reactions in the mitochondria produce most of the cell's energy.
Answer: TRUE

4) Digestion of a polysaccharide is an anabolic process.
Answer: FALSE

5) The production of carbon dioxide and water in the body is an anabolic process.
Answer: FALSE

6) ATP is the primary energy source for the cell.
Answer: TRUE

7) Catabolic reactions provide energy to generate ATP in the cell.
Answer: TRUE

8) The conversion of ATP to ADP and inorganic phosphate produces 7.3 kcal/mole of energy.
Answer: TRUE

9) Oxidation involves the gain of electrons for a substance.
Answer: FALSE

10) NAD^+ acts as a hydrogen acceptor in metabolic reactions.
Answer: TRUE

11) FADH$_2$ is the oxidized form of FAD.

Answer: FALSE

12) The production of new triacylglycerols is termed ketosis.

Answer: FALSE

13) Ammonium ions and carbon dioxide produce urea in the urea cycle.

Answer: TRUE

14) The urea cycle is the major pathway for eliminating the excess nitrogen from amino acid degradation.

Answer: TRUE

15) Chylomicrons consist of bile salts and lipids.

Answer: FALSE

16) Protein digestion begins in the small intestine.

Answer: FALSE

17) Carbohydrate digestion begins in the mouth.

Answer: TRUE

18) In the chemiosmotic model, protons flow through ATP synthase.

Answer: TRUE

18.5 Matching Questions

Indicate the amount of ATP produced when each of the following reactions occurs.

1) complete oxidation of glucose   A) 3 ATP

2) Acetyl CoA $\rightarrow$ 2CO$_2$ B) 2 ATP

3) glucose $\rightarrow$ 2 pyruvate under   C) 36 ATP
   aerobic conditions
                                                    D) 12 ATP
4) glucose $\rightarrow$ 2 lactate
                                                    E) 6 ATP
5) pyruvate $\rightarrow$ acetyl CoA +
   CO$_2$

1) C   2) D   3) E   4) B   5) A

Match the terms with the following descriptions.

6) the process that makes ATP   A) oxidative phosphorylation
   using energy from the
   electron transport chain   B) coenzyme A

7) the carrier of acetyl
   (two–carbon) groups

6) A   7) B

Identify each of the following metabolic pathways.

8) digestion

9) triacylglycerol hydrolysis

10) the conversion of glucose to pyruvic acid

11) the series of reactions that converts acetyl CoA to carbon dioxide and water

12) the series of reactions that produces water

13) the series of reactions that uses electron carriers

14) the conversion of fatty acids to 2-carbon units of acetyl Coenzyme A

15) the conversion of an amino acid to an α-keto acid

16) the removal of an amino group as NH_4^+ from glutamic acid to yield α-ketoglutaric acid

A) glycolysis

B) breaking down of macromolecules

C) β-oxidation

D) transamination

E) citric acid cycle

F) oxidative deamination

G) electron transport

H) lipid metabolism

8) B   9) H   10) A   11) E   12) G   13) G
14) C   15) D   16) F

250

Match the following.

17) compounds produced when there is little or no carbohydrate metabolism and a subsequent increase in fat metabolism

18) a carrier of electrons to the site of ATP production, from oxidation reactions involving carbon–carbon double bonds

19) lipoproteins formed from triacylglycerols and protein

20) a major step in fatty acid degradation

21) a condition of low blood pH

22) the main source of energy in the body

23) a carrier of 2–carbon units in fatty acid degradation

A) chylomicrons

B) acidosis

C) ATP

D) alkalosis

E) ketone bodies

F) GTP

G) β-oxidation

H) FAD

I) Coenzyme A.

17) E   18) H   19) A   20) G   21) B   22) C
23) I